Kama Sutra
for Women

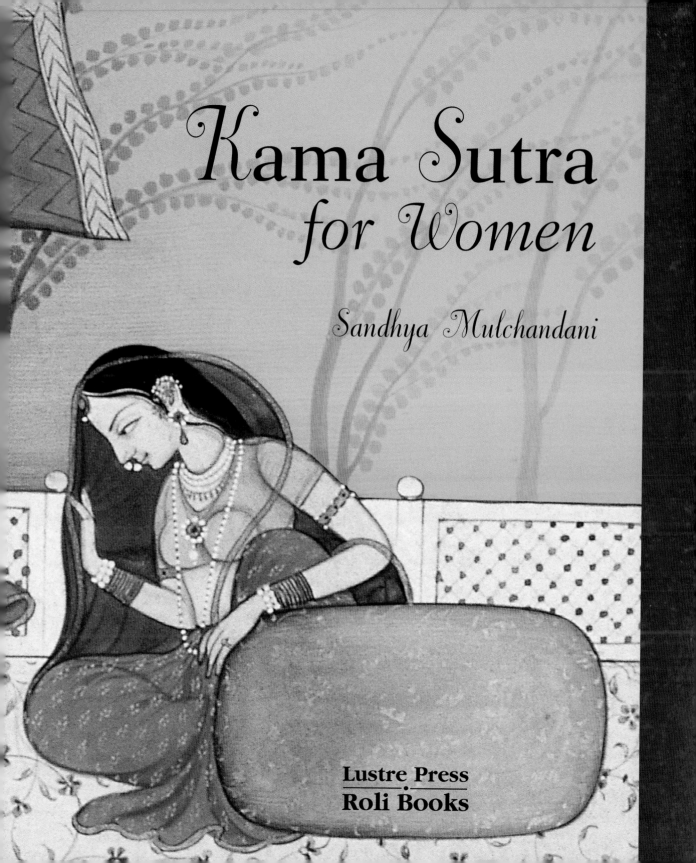

Kama Sutra
for Women

Sandhya Mulchandani

Lustre Press
Roli Books

Contents

Introduction
Vatsyayana's Kama Sutra

Because they belong to the same species, men and women should seek the same pleasure in sexual relations. A women therefore, should learn the Kama Sutra or at least part of it by studying its practice…

*I*n the beginning, there was desire, which was the first seed of the 'mind', says the Rg Veda. Hindu cosmology believes that the process of creation emerged from a primordial chaos of frenzied disorder. This devolution became, over time, the traditional Indian view of creation and was manifested as erotic hierophany making the universe a sacred creation that is essentially erotic as well.

This was how the ancient Aryans viewed their world as they made an intimate connection with nature. Just as the earth bore grain, the trees bore fruit and the animals produced young ones, these men and women indulged in their desires and marvelled at the miracle of birth, rejoicing in the sexuality that made such creation possible.

Viewed as a prerequisite for existence, the pursuit of the pleasures of the human body was one way of contemplating the spiritual union that one aspired for. The need to apprehend *Ananda* (bliss) as well as the pursuit and an understanding of *Sukha* (pleasure and happiness), which included sexual pleasure, became a subject of rigorous inquiry. Human sexuality was thus viewed by the Aryans with awe and wonder, and the coming together of a man and woman was considered magical. The need to fully comprehend, explore and sustain these magical moments became an end in itself. Curiosity led to contemplation, and the study of human sexuality became a basis for human existence, with the thread of sexuality embedded deep into its fabric.

Indian philosophy and religion have often been rebuked for being other worldly, and its followers unkindly depicted as devoted to cross-legged and cross-eyed trances. This misinformed stereotype sidesteps one seminal point: the vital engagement of Hindu religion and philosophy with the mundane world to such an extent that they do not, ostrich-like, eschew desire but include it as one of the aims of life and

fulfilment. Indeed, legend has it that the *Kama Shastras* were the topic of the debate between India's greatest religious reformer and spiritual teacher, Shri Adi Shankaracharya and Bharati the wife of a Vedic ritualist named Mandana Mishra. Shri Adi Shankaracharya, who journeyed across India vanquishing its best scholars in debate and winning them over as disciples, was unable to answer Bharati's questions about the erotic arts and sciences. Admitting that true wisdom must include an understanding of all aspects of life, the pious celibate asked to be excused from the debate for a month in order to master the theory and practice of love.

However, Hindus did not confine themselves to the study of love in isolation, but chose to explore the entire range of refinements that made life worthwhile. According to ancient wisdom, the life of a human being was directed to three goals (*trivarga*): The striving for good *Dharma* or right conduct; useful *Artha* or material possessions and well-being, and *Kama*, love and the associated pleasures of the senses. Practising these three aspects of life made it possible to lead a meaningful and joyous life both in this world and the next. Thus, everything in life is a function of the 'proper place, time and person', or *desa*, *kala* and *patra*. By casting these aspects in the right combination, one could discover the meaning and beauty of life and relationships. The stress was on integration, for neglecting any one of these areas would lead to a diminished stability

and dangerous imbalance. Ancient Indian literature addresses a great number of scientific questions. Treatises on Astronomy, Geometry, Phonetics, Metrics, Grammar, Medicine, Politics, Men and Morals were written in the belief that if a thing is worth doing, it is worth doing well.

Erotology thus became a science, a *shastra*. The senses were perceived as being a refinement of the physical on a higher plane of consciousness and sex embraced as an integral part of a full and complete life. So the ancients studied sex, practised and dissected it, classified its many methods, shared their knowledge about techniques and passed on what they had learnt. They explored not merely the physicality of intercourse but examined its pleasures and pitfalls— impotency, unequal expectations, *Shringara* (the art of adornment) and the sixty-four branches of fine arts, virility and aphrodisiacs, etiquette and manners, townsmen and courtesans. Thus they covered every conceivable aspect of society. The more the ancients researched and commented, collected and classified, the more their work became obscure. This is how the erotic texts of India developed a mythology of their own.

Between the 2nd and 4th centuries AD, a celibate monk called Vatsyayana, planned an extract of the whole subject into a single comprehensive shorter work that would cater to society at large. This

was also a time when peace reigned, society prospered and leisure was common, when the intrigue of romance and exploring sensuality caught the imagination of the people. Although widely viewed today as merely a manual that describes impossible sexual positions and the techniques of intercourse, the *Kama Sutra* provides a window to an ancient Hindu heritage very different from the one conveyed in most philosophical, historical and religious discourses. It gives glimpses of the social, cultural and erotic life of a people who were energetic, life-affirming, tolerant and surprisingly far ahead of their times. The often-exaggerated sexual religiosity found in the scriptures, art, painting, poetry and literature of the period is clearly an expression of the vigorous sexuality of a society that considered sexual activity almost a religious duty. Reinforcing attitudes towards sexuality from a bygone era, Vatsyayana's work thus became a definitive manifesto of a highly evolved culture.

Vatsyayana did not restrict himself to the interplay between man and woman as seen by the seven books of the *Kama Sutra*—General Principles, Sexual Union, Courtship and Marriage, the Wife, Seducing the Wives of Others, Courtesans, and Erotic Lore. Ancient India was primarily heterosexual, and marriage came to be celebrated as one of the

Curiosity led to contemplation and the study of sexuality became a basis for human existence.

first logical goals in a respectable and safe relationship between lovers. Monogamy was the norm rather than the exception and based on mutual respect, love, faith and the right to seek mutual sexual fulfilment. However the sages of ancient India understood that an absence of sexual happiness in even an otherwise happy marriage would lead to experimentation outside of the institution and result in a multiplicity of partners. Adultery was thus not uncommon.

Hindu mythology itself has innumerable stories illustrating the manner in which gods themselves often indulged in adulterous thoughts and actions. In keeping with the social milieu of the time, where courtesans (*ganikas*) were a respected and an accepted part of social life as were temporary relationships, contractual arrangements, relationships with housemaids, and pleasure houses run by women trained in the art and craft of love, the *Kama Sutra* goes into great detail about the process of seduction of *parkiya* (women who are not one's own). Neither are other aspects of sexuality ignored—same-sex love was not wholly unknown and the text explores all other gender perspectives—men, women, homosexuals, lesbians, prostitutes, and eunuchs or persons of the 'third nature'.

The principles of erotic art concern the daughters of kings and ministers and courtesans which is why in an ideal society women must study and practice the Kama Sutra.

Women were not content to be passive partners and demanded that their orgasmic potential be satisfied.

Vedic India is often quoted as being a landmark in the history of Indian womanhood. Though Vedic society was patriarchal and male-dominated, yet in matters of pleasure, the sexes were seen as equal. The needs of both men and women were addressed in the belief that without the magic of mutual pleasure and satisfaction, sex was dead or lifeless. The emphasis was on mutual pleasure and Vatsyayana had no need to emphasize equality, it was already a matter of custom and social grace. His work does not champion the cause of women, for when it was written—women were treated as equals and sexual intercourse recognized as being more than fleeting gratification. As Vatsyayana himself states, 'Because they belong to the same species, man and woman seek the same pleasure in sexual relations.' The well-bred townsman for whom the *Kama Sutra* was written was advised to consider the satisfaction of his mistress as carefully as his own, for she was as passionate as himself and in some instances more so.

The enduring power of the *Kama Sutra* is its modernity, and its ability to understand—nearly two millennia before feminists appealed for a woman's larger (or rightful) share and participation in life that sexuality is not the preserve of one gender. Today, sexuality is often used as a weapon of power. Man and woman encircle, overpower and lock each other in the prison of aberrant sexual conduct that often results in violence and unhappiness. The very first casualty in a troubled relationship is the death of sexual pleasure. Vatsyayana's *Kama Sutra* is an equal opportunity pleasure provider with no games or power play between the sexes. 'Men look for love, women too look for love: women play the main role in the act of intercourse,' he said. Vatsyayana taught men to appreciate an empowered female lover, who is ready to explore her potential, revels in her body and welcomes sexual pleasure for in doing so uninhibitedly, she creates energies that catapult both lovers to heights of ecstasy.

Therefore, women were not content to be purely passive partners but expected and demanded that their orgasmic potential and sexual happiness be satisfied. Armed with sanction from the scriptures, they expressed themselves sexually without hesitation, were uninhibited about displaying their passions and often took on assertive roles in sexual relationships. They were encouraged to seek orgasms, taught about their anatomy—G-spots and all—and made aware of the days and times of the month when they would derive the most pleasure. The text, therefore focuses, encourages and educates men to be skilful and sensitive lovers. Concentrating on the art of seduction and foreplay and the importance of giving pleasure to women, the text goes over in great detail the art of courtship, romance, the need to create a sexual ambience, the techniques and positions that would maximize pleasure and bring women to orgasm.

Vatsyayana, however, believed that the working as well as the consciousness of pleasure in men and women were different—that in most instances, the males assumed the lead role, while women assumed subordinate roles; that women tended to get aroused slowly. Believing that disparities would lead to unhappiness, the emphasis was that one should only seek a relationship with one's own type be it in temperament, emotional make up, expectations or physical structure. In order to discover one's type of personality, Vatsyayana categorized every aspect of human life.

First, men are said to be of different types, depending upon the length and thickness of their *lingam* or phallus. Similarly, women are differentiated according to the varying depth of their *yoni*, or vagina. Based on this there are, accordingly, nine types of union between men and women of different proportions. Besides, there are nine types of unions, according to the intensity or strength of passion. Kissing falls into four categories. Every kind of embrace is similarly given a distinct name. There are sixty-four different positions that can be assumed during intercourse. Vatsyayana dealt with methods of sexual play using the lips, tongue, and mouth, introduction to the joys of anal intercourse, pragmatic ways of dealing with sexual problems using special techniques, toys, and love potions. The question is: can a treatise enhance sexual performance? Clearly, technique is no substitute for passion. As Vatsyayana himself puts it: '...the texts are of help only till passion is not excited: but once the wheel of sexual ecstasy starts to roll, there is then no need for any Shastra or order.'

Vatsyayana made another fundamental observation—that in any relationship, the sexual impulse at the outset is predominantly egotistical. He thus foresaw that if relationships were to blossom, men

needed to be unselfish or altruistic. Without an understanding of what the partner desired and working to meet that demand, all courtship was doomed to failure. Thus he urged more skilled and longer love play. His book teaches men to appreciate the different dispositions and temperament of women towards sex. It extols the virtue of generosity when it comes to giving in love and guides the uninitiated male lover into the kinds of intimacy and subtlety that so many women crave. 'The *Kama Sutra's* most valuable insight, is that pleasure needs to be cultivated, that in the realm of sex, nature requires culture,' says Dr. Sudhir Kakkar in his new translation of the *Kama Sutra*.

The accent on mutual pleasure is inherent in the word *sambhoga*, which literally translates not merely as intercourse, but as 'mutual pleasure'. Thus reciprocity became a keynote in the art of making love. Vatsyayana says: 'Every lover must reciprocate the beloved's gesture with equal intensity, kiss for kiss and embrace with embrace. If there is no reciprocity, the beloved will feel dejected and consider the lover as a stone-pillar. It will result in a highly unsatisfactory union. To keep the passion alive and inflamed, reciprocity is absolutely essential.' Above all, Vatsyayana says: 'At all times, the man must carefully observe every action of the woman he loves, and so gauge her passion and preferences, and act accordingly, to give her the greatest pleasure.' The *Kama Sutra* thus became a guide that provided an awkward man with the technique to make love more sensuously, and taught a woman how to kindle desire so that society could fully comprehend and participate in *Kama Krida* or the Game of Love.

This code book of love laid out the manner and mode as well as the other attendants of desire. The setting up of a tryst, the use of maidens and go-betweens, types of perfume, the dress code, the demeanour to be adopted, as well as the food to be offered. The principles of *Kama* also required a woman to respect herself and take great care of her body and its well-being. Good looks, a pleasing personality, youth and liberality were seen as necessary feminine qualities to attract a man. In the absence of these, the *Kama Sutra* advises both men and women to seek the help of artifice. The text abounds in details of cosmetics and beauty care, perfumes and clothing, jewellery and deportment.

The science of beauty—the doctrine of *alamkara* or ornamentation and *rasa* especially of *shringara rasa* or the essence (or mood) of allurement is an enduring part of the Indian ethos, an aesthetic experience that permeated every aspect of human endeavour. These preoccupations with beauty and sexuality of ancient and medieval India are abundantly found in its art, poetry, literature and sculpture. Those who view Hinduism as an ascetic religion could well be profoundly disturbed. Yet the ascetic strain that runs in Indian society has always maintained a dialectic relationship with the sensual. In a culture where there was an urge to seek a reality more real than that offered by mere intellectual experience, art in all its forms, was dedicated to the service of an ideal philosophy. Interestingly, in several instances, the ideal was the erotic. The sculptures in the temples of Khajuraho and Konarak, which are influenced by it, seem to mock at modern prudery. The Indian temple, which perhaps depicts the ultimate coming together of the sacred and the sensuous, represented the breaking of the very last taboo with its expressive depictions of romantic maithuna figures. The most intimate and personal of human interactions were sculpted in stone, in full public view. For some, this represented decadence and a regression from spiritual purity—for others, it was a sign of remarkable advance: a living and unashamed acceptance of the fact that society had been able to break down the shackles of hypocritical prudery. Yet no matter how this was viewed, it demonstrated in a very powerful way that at

that time, Indian religion and its monumental expression were based not on worldly denial, but on an unabashed acceptance of essential human urges.

Such a wide platform inspired telling and brilliant images in art. By not confining art and restricting the imagination of the artist, the *Kama sutra* had the wholesome effect of taking Indian art to every corner of the human psyche and making it explore all the stages where social discourse on pleasure takes place—the kingly court, the noble's mansion, the maiden's boudoir, the secret garden, the moonlit night.

These stages were most poetically portrayed in Indian miniature painting, which was based, like much of Indian art, on the theory of *rasa*. In its widest sense, *rasa* is the depiction of a mood that matches one of the nine essences of life—the *nava rasas*. The *rasa* theory is the bedrock of Indian art and nowhere is it seen as vividly as in the world of the Indian miniature painting which became a potent medium for the expression of visual fantasies. The depiction of the *nayika* or a beautiful young woman in her myriad moods as she goes out to meet her lover or *nayak*, the anticipation on the face of a lover who is waiting for his beloved, the sexual energies during intercourse, were all noted and expressed in minute detail. Nature provided the backdrop against which much of this human drama was enacted. Birds and bowers, rain-filled clouds and vines and most importantly the coming of *Phalgun*, or spring, seen as the playing ground of Lord Kamadev himself were depicted with loving grace by Indian artists to convey a sense of joy and wonder, or a mood of unspoiled romance and eroticism.

Central to all this was the woman, seen paradoxically as mistress and mother, as both goddess and *ganika*. An old Sanskrit poem talking about the attributes of a woman has this to say: 'In the performance of duty, she must be a well-trained servant, in giving advice she must be wise as a prince's counsellor, in appearance she must resemble Lakshmi, in poverty she must be a prudent housewife, in affection she must be devoted like a mother, in the bed-chamber she must be fascinating as a courtesan—these are the six indispensable qualities of the ideal woman.' The Shastras thus talk of the *Catushasti-kala* or sixty-four arts that were required reading in syllabus of education.

In ancient India, the pursuit of art was not left to the mercy of occasional sparks of inspiration or individual taste, especially in the case of women. These were considered necessities that prepared a girl to be a good wife as well as a good lover. Thus the girl would learn to sing, play musical instruments, dance, write, compose poetry, arrange flowers artistically, cook, and learn to be a good lover. Women from various walks of life—wives, courtesans, unmarried women, young girls, sisters—were advised to learn the intricacies of physical intimacy. A girl was required to know at least sixteen arts before she presented herself to her husband: reading others' thoughts, expressions of love, showing acceptance through body postures, allowing the slow touching of her body, scratching lovingly with her nails, biting gently, undoing the hook of her lower garments seductively, straightening and exposing her private parts, actively participating in intercourse, pleasing the partner, getting full satisfaction and ensuring the same for her partner, encouraging the partner for intercourse, posing as if angry, removing anger in a playful way, pleasing the angry partner, leaving the sleeping partner, going to sleep after intercourse, and so on.

Thus instructed, the young girls were capable of not just satisfying their husbands, but able to differentiate between constructive and destructive sexual desires. The *Kama Sutra* plays the role of advisor and mentor, warning and advising women on all the facets of their relationships, be it attracting men, fobbing them off pleasantly, entertaining them, or changing them!

The enduring lesson of Vatsyayana's *Kama Sutra* is that relationships require attention: if sex is not to become a reflexive act of habit. Clearly, the biggest threat to sex comes from ennui, keeping sexual interest alive is an enormous challenge. That despite a modern idiom, overt sexuality, contraception, education and abortion, the gap of twenty centuries notwithstanding, the relationship between a man and a woman was and continues to be based on understanding intimacy, the need to please, keeping the sexual frisson alive and the knowledge to do so.

The forthrightness of Vatsyayana's *Kama Sutra* is absent in today's permissive society. He talks about things we are too ashamed or embarrassed to talk about even today. This is also why although the *Kama Sutra* is famous for its description of sexual positions, its psychological insights into the emotional patterns between men and women are no less compelling. How do you treat a depressed man? How does a woman beg off when a lover demands sex and she is not in the mood? How does a woman take control of a man who is attracted to other women as well? Feminism notwithstanding, a vast section of women are still to experience the pleasures of orgasm and remain locked into dysfunctional relationships. The text addresses these modern day

However submissive or reticent a woman may be by nature, she is quick at learning the games of love.

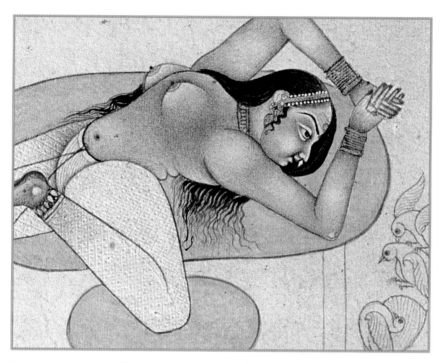

insecurities as well as how to deal effectively with the realities of dysfunctional sexuality, adultery, prostitution, homosexuality, group sex and cross-dressing. In contrast to the culture of third century India, we react to biological forces and social conventions with a lack of consciousness and immature behaviour resulting in sexual harassment, rape, perversions, sexual abuse, violence within marriages and child molestation. In an age where a woman has more choices than ever before, she should be prepared, confident and firm in her knowledge that the choices that she is making are the right ones. At the centre of all unhappiness is the conflict between unfulfilled desires and the ability to realize them. To explore one's potential free from fear, self-consciousness, and inhibitions, should be a fundamental right of mankind.

Desire, romance and eroticism and a passion for living: these are the essential elements of the *Kama Sutra*. These fundamental and unchangeable human attributes mirror every individual's hopes and expectations. In this sense, the *Kama Sutra* is at once the oldest and most modern of books. Perhaps this is the secret of its enduring appeal.

At the centre of all unhappiness is the conflict between unfullfiled desires and the ability to realize them. To explore one's potential free from inhibition and fear should be the fundamental right of mankind.

25

Shringara
The Art of Attraction

If kama is considered to be the foundation of life, then shringara which leads to the acme of pleasure is the bedrock of the aesthetic experience and, metaphorically, of the mystical experience...

*A*dhering to the path of *Dharma* gave man meaning and a sense of purpose to his existence; following the tenets of *Artha* gave him the means to achieve, righteously, a comfortable live and standing in society; the study of *Kama* provided the means and ways of enjoying his life to its fullest extent within the prescribed parameters. Vatsyayana himself concludes his magnum opus by clearly stating that, 'this work is not intended to be used as an instrument for merely satisfying our desires. A person, acquainted with the true principles of this science, who preserves his *Dharma*, *Artha*, and *Kama*, and has regard for the practices of the people, is sure to obtain mastery over his senses.'

The two pillars of hedonism must surely be sexuality and civility; even those who value the erotic must ensure that it does not infringe upon the rights of others. Although pleasure is primary, yet its pursuit has to always be tempered with sensitivity, common sense, reverence for life, and consideration for others and above all else, self control. 'One cannot live pleasantly without living wisely and nobly.' So the wise men of yore advocated ways to become a 'complete man'—men who were equally adept at understanding the *Arthashastra*, the *Dharma Sutras* as well as the *Kama Shastras*. Unlike the scriptures and other Vedic texts that were restricted to Brahmanical scholars, even young maidens were encouraged to study the subject of *Kama* along with its arts and sciences before marriage. Vatsyayana was of the opinion that since women anyway knew and learnt about sex through personal experience, their studying it was imperative not just as the practice of a science but to understand the rules and laws on which this science is based.

Sure enough, women, such as daughters of princes and their ministers, courtesans and other public women all actually became

versed in the *Kama Shastra*. *Grihini sacivah sakhi mithah priyasisya lalite kalavidhau*—this is how the immortal lover Aja remembers his dearly beloved Queen Indumati in Kalidasa's *Raghuvamsa*. The woman was not just the mistress of a man's household but was also his friend, philosopher and guide, his most intimate companion in happiness and woe alike, and the perfect collaborator in the pursuit of all that was worthy. So the pursuit of the finer aspects of life gradually became an important feature of civilization, wherein every cultivated person sought artistic expression spanning a variety of interests. In music and painting, in dancing and acting, in architecture and sculpture the basic idea of *rasa* took seed and became the essence of every branch of fine art.

What exactly is *'rasa'*? Loosely translated as flavour, pleasure or to relish, *rasa* is not an objective quality in art but a spiritual activity, for to appreciate a work of art is to savour its aesthetic quality and experience its taste. When poetry, literature song and dance evoke sensuous images and stimulates the emotions than the artiste fulfils the criterion of *rasa*. This was not affective in kind, nor is it dependent on any specific subject but arises from a perfect aesthetic experience,

The paradox of sexuality is that the conditions of a satisfactory union lie outside sex—they lie in the art of enhancing pleasure.

one that can realize the embodied spirit. Whether in art or architecture, singing or sex, to achieve excellence it must stimulate a person's sensitivities and arouse a desire to know and experience more. The *Kama Sutra* believed that aesthetics was ecstasy as distinct from mere enjoyment of loveliness.

Occupying pride of place amongst these and known as *Raja Rasa*, the king of *rasas* is *Shringara* or the erotic sentiment. Traditionally, the arts are classified into *Nava Rasas* based on nine different emotions or moods; these nine sentiments are *Shringara*/love, *Hasya*/laughter, *Karuna*/sadness, *Raudra*/anger, *Vira*/pride, *Hayanaka*/fear, *Bibhatsa*/disgust, *Adbhut*/wonder and *Shanta*/peace. Not only was each raga associated with a particular mood, but it was also connected to a particular time of the day, year and season.

The *Nava Rasas* set the foundation and the arts proliferated. The resulting sixty-four arts were conceived as channels of creative energy, considered direct emanations from the goddess Saraswati, responsible in Indian mythology for learning besides being the muse for all the arts. 'The sixty-four arts are like the flames of an inner sun, blazing from the solar plexus, burning up negativity. These flames of creativity

From the shringara rasa *comes many things*—vilas, kama, bhakthi, *and eventually even* moksha.

31

purify the psyche and bring about an inner transformation.' The number sixty-four in itself was also believed to be auspicious, being a legendary arithmetical figure in India, so that besides these branches of arts, there were sixty-four Mayas, sixty-four Yoginis, sixty-four Mudras, and so on.

Besides inner well-being, as practical skills these arts delighted kings and noblemen, men and women alike bringing money, fame, and recognition and, of course, pleasure. Thus, carefully cultivated, the pursuit of the arts was not left to chance, inspiration, individual taste or experience. *Catuhsasti-kala* or the sixty-four arts became an integral part of the curriculum and syllabus. The arts were not restricted to women; the *Srimad Bhagavatam* talks about how Lord Krishna and his brother Balarama learnt the techniques of these sixty-four arts in just sixty-four days. Thus *Vyavamavida* (physical exercise), *Ayudha* (use of weapons), *Rathacarya* (proficiency in driving a chariot), *Gajaprstha* (elephant riding), *Vadya* (the playing of musical instruments), *Nrytta* (dancing), *Gandharvaveda* (the art of music and dance), *Turangavayojnana* (skill in examining a horse and determining its age), *Purusalaksana* (ways in which to understand human nature), *Citrakarman* (painting), *Patracchedya* (decoration), *Lekhyakarman* (engraving), *Sarva dyutakala* (proficiency in gambling), *Grahaganita* (astronomy), *Ratnapariksa* (appraising jewels), *Dantavyapara* (ivory carving), *Vastuvidya* (the study of Vaastu), were but a few disciplines in which men and women of the time sought to become proficient.

Skill in at least some of the sixty-four arts were a woman's credentials, especially when she became of marriageable age, an indication of whether she would make a good wife and enthusiastic lover. Prudence in housekeeping, hygiene of the body and mind, braiding of hair and dyeing them with henna—were all considered to be general arts that prepared a girl to be a good wife. Apart from this, there was the question of physical intimacy. For this there were sixteen separate arts that a young girl had to master before being presented in front of her husband.

These were—gauging others' reactions and thoughts—displaying passion through gestures, permitting different parts of her body to be touched, scratching gently with her nails, biting, removing her clothes

A girl should display her skill in the practice of the arts by her right conduct and right knowledge. Equally a man skilled in the sixty-four arts is looked upon with love by his wife, by the wives of others, as well as by courtesans.

seductively, enthusiastic participation in intercourse, pleasuring her partner, stimulating as well as achieving orgasm, initiating the game of love, seducing her husband playfully, among others. Apart from these, there were other ways in which the girl would entice her lover, alternatively seducing and spurring him, cajoling him and neglecting him, playing hard to get while flirting with him… in short, keeping her lover intrigued and interested. Indeed, Vatsyayana's list of the arts to be cultivated by a man and a woman, as essential to the fulfilment of the *Kama* experience is so very long that one might feel completely discouraged. At first read it sounds almost absurd for what is demanded of men and women is that they be proficient charioteers, architects, metallurgists, magicians and many other things before they be good lovers. But this is obviously not the case. As one commentary on the *Kama Sutra* puts it, 'It is only that Vatsyayana wants us to become aware of the paradox of sexuality; that the conditions for a satisfying union lie outside sex. Sex as energy simultaneously requires the flow from other forms of energy, without which it will diminish, and die.'

Therefore, one of the major aphorisms of love is the need to orchestrate everything for the enhancement of pleasure. If one has to create and sustain magic in a relationship, it requires more than a fleeting encounter with one another's genitals. So the art of making love requires cultivating a wider area of sensibilities, such as music, dance, poetry, literature. But as a very first step it takes a man and woman who were endowed with good qualities.

Qualities of a Good Man

Those skilled in the arts, poets, story tellers, eloquent men, possessed of great minds, energy, visionaries, those who are perseverant, devoted, free from anger, liberal, affectionate to parents, sociable, skilled in completing verses begun by others, sportsmen, healthy, strong, brave, not addicted to drinking, with sexual prowess, respectful to women, wealthy, free from envy, and lastly free from suspicion. These are the qualities of a good man.

The Ideal Woman

A woman should be beautiful, amenable, with a good body and enjoy wealth. She should enthusiastically participate in sexual intercourse and have the same desires as her man. She should be knowledgeable and interested in educating herself, free from greed, be sociable and interested in the arts. Moreover she should be intelligent, of good disposition have good manners and be straightforward in her behaviour. Women who were loud, mean, laughed loudly, possessed of malignity, anger, avarice, dullness, sloth and stupidity were to be avoided. Once the woman became a wife, her conduct and behaviour had to be exemplary:

The Conduct of a Wife

When the wife appears in front of her husband, she should always be well dressed, wearing jewellery and flowers and be perfumed with sweet-smelling ointments or scents. She should observe the necessary rituals, fasts and vows for her husband. She should be a careful housekeeper, stocking up on commodities during different times of the year when these are cheap and be careful with money. She should neither disclose nor talk about her husband's wealth and be discreet about the secrets that she shares with her husband. She should strive to surpass other women of her own rank with her intelligence, appearance, her competence as a cook, her demeanour and in the service of her husband. She should be sociable, welcome her husband's friends and be respectful to her in-laws. Women who are vain, too self-absorbed, greedy, loud and disrespectful are to be avoided.

Once the man and woman had these basic qualities, it was imperative that they cultivate a proficiency in the arts. The *Kama Sutra* lists these 64 arts in great detail, several of which concentrate on beauty and the decoration of the body. Others are more pedestrian: such as carpentry, metal working, lathe working, while knowledge about mining, deciphering ciphers, architecture, arithmetic and logic were definite indications of the level and calibre of the people it addressed. However, the underlying message seems to be that if a thing is worth doing, it is worth doing well.

Some of the more important arts listed in the *Kama Sutra* are:

Music

The first amongst the fine arts is considered to be music. The *Chandogya Upanishad* calls music the *Devajanavidya* or the Knowledge of the Gods. The *Puranas*, also clearly show that a close relationship existed between religion and music as early as 1000 B.C.E, and was considered to be a representation of divine beauty, a mediator between the spiritual and sensual life. A universal language often used to express beauty and joy, pathos and as prayer, music elevates the soul to a higher plane, making it possible to directly seek the divine. Learning and appreciating music naturally elevates a human being, making him more attuned to emotional nuances and thus more humane. The feminine aspect of a raga is known as the *ragini* and is synonymous with the *nayika* or heroine in art and literature.

Dance

Closely associated with music is dance that has been defined as a motion that arises from emotion. With its natural appetite for rhythm the human body responds naturally to any vibrating sound. In India, the *Natya Shastras* as propounded by Bharata became the touchstone of this ancient art form. The relationship of the body, senses, mind, intellect

and soul are all interlinked and is regarded by Hindus as the abode of the divine. Therefore a beautiful body was seen as a temple of god and dance a medium for invoking the divine within. Considered to be a yoga, dance reflects the highest order of spiritual discipline, a medium that evokes the supreme state of bliss as well as a vehicle for seeking enlightenment. Thus viewed, the dancer became an integral part of ritual worship in temples. Dance was thus seen as opening up multi-dimensional realms of communication and connectedness of expression, which made it a very valuable skill.

Painting and Sculpture

The *Navarasa bhava* found full expression in painting and sculpture. The *rasa* theory became the bedrock of Indian art and was best expressed in Indian miniature paintings. With its own rules, miniature painting was a potent medium for the expression of visual fantasies. Indian artists often depicted birds and flowers, trees and creepers with a loving grace. In the miniature paintings from Mewar or the Kangra Valley, idyllic nature scenes were created to convey a sense of joy and wonder, or a mood of unspoiled romance and eroticism. As was seen in the case of such themes as *nayika bheda* (differentiation of heroes and heroines) or the ragamala paintings, which took their cue from structural melodies, desire and devotion are combined in ingenious ways. The same sentiment also found expression in stone especially in temples like Khajuraho and Konarak where *Kama* merged with *Rasa* to form one of the most celebrated art forms that India has ever known.

Culinary Skills

Amongst all the domestic arts, pride of place is occupied by the art of the palate. Housewives who won the hearts of their husbands through their stomachs are legion. In ancient India, a good cook held an honoured place in society; Draupadi was acknowledged to be a very good cook, as were Bhima and King Nala. Proficiency in cooking, imagination in serving a meal and catering to one's husband and his guests were and are still upheld as supreme virtues in India.

Chewing Paan

The word '*tambula*' occurs with regular frequency in most *Kama Shastra* texts being closely associated as a form of foreplay when the nayak and nayika first meet. The *Kama Sutra* says: 'Only after cleaning the teeth and having looked into the mirror and having eaten a *tambula* to render fragrance to the mouth, should a person start his day's work'. *Tambula*, which is basically a betel nut wrapped in a paan leaf is a Sanskrit word that derives its name from the word *tamra* (copper), indicating red colour. According to Sushruta, the patriarch of ancient Indian Ayurveda, paan keeps the mouth clean, strengthens the voice, tongue and teeth, guards against diseases besides being a digestive. Early Sanskrit texts mention the consumption of betel leaf among the eight enjoyments, the others being incenses, women, clothes, music, bed and food. Offered in ritual and to the gods, Vatsyayana included the *tambula* as one of the *solah shringar* or 16 items of toiletries.

Solah Shringar: *The Sixteen Adornments of a Woman*

Ancient texts identify sixteen different embellishments (*solah-shringar*), used to celebrate the beauty and divinity of the female form. In Hindu arithmetic, sixteen is a significant number corresponding to the sixteen phases of the moon, which in turn is associated with a woman's menstrual cycle. Thus a young woman of sixteen is considered to be the embodiment of perfection, since she is at the peak of her physical charms. The term *Shringar* is also associated with Sri, another name for Laksmi, the goddess of female beauty, luck, prosperity and fertility who is venerated as an ideal wife. Women realized the spiritual side of ornamentation and believed that by adorning their bodies, they also satisfied a universal longing for the embellishment of its intangible counterpart: the human spirit.

Thus, women continue to embellish their bodies as a means of expressing their own aesthetic sentiments and to attract men. These stages of dressing up are also known as the Body Decoration Arts, the study of decorating the body, whose sixteen stages serve a specific purpose: that of being utilitarian as well as decorative. These are variously known as:

Nepathyayoga

Nepathya undertakes the study of what we now call couture, that is fashion, fabrics and the art of dressing up to maximize and

enhance one's assets. Since this pre-supposes a sense of drama, the art of making up for the stage and theatre was also included under this head.

Karnapatrabhanga

This has to do with the decoration of the ears. The different types of ornaments like earrings, loops, flowers which were initially made out of ivory, conch shells, leaves and flowers were replaced with metals like iron and then silver, gold and precious gems. According to some scholars, the art of painting the forehead, over the eyebrows, and other parts of the face up to the ear with sandal paste, vermilion amongst others, are also known as *Karnapatrabhanga*. No woman in India ever went without earrings. Especially on wedding and festival days, the jewellery was so elaborate, that chains passing over the crown of the head were needed to support the earlobes. Such elaborate jewellery, besides being beautiful in itself, was meant to enhance the beauty of a woman.

Bhusana-yojana

Bhusana-yojana or the making of gold jewellery. Ornaments were considered to be of two varieties: the first included those which are strung on a thread: for instance, garlands of jewels, gems, pearls or other valuable stones. From the earliest times, the stringing together of flowers was an art—garlands were offered in temples and were an important part of the evening-dress of both men and women. This continues to be a ritual—the exchange of garlands during a wedding ceremony and as a mark of respect—a common custom even today is to welcome an honoured guest with a garland. The other category included ornaments which are not thread woven. Made of metals like gold and silver that were melted, these were mixed with other materials for adding colour and resilience and then cast into different shapes. Ornaments like bangles, armlets, earrings, necklaces, waist belts were made by this process.

Facing page: *Elegance is a matter of the quality of clothes and jewellery. So both men and women should be bedecked with jewels and garlands made either from precious gems or flowers.*

Sekharakapida-yojana

Though closely linked to the *Bhusana-yojana*, this is a very specialized art of making ornaments using only flowers. *Sekharaka* denotes a type of flower ornament that is placed at the back of the head, that is on the 'Sikhasthana' and is then made to hang and encircle the neck like a *jhumka* (dangling earring). Besides this rather elaborate and intricately strung ornament, the hair was plaited with flowers from the top of the head right to the tip, intricate designs made to look as they were made of gold and silver, depicting the sun and moon were worn on the top of the head. Flowers were woven into elaborate bracelets, bangles and *bajubands* (armlets), waist bands from fresh jasmine emphasized the beauty of the thin waist besides adding fragrance.

Visesakachhedya

Visesakachhedya is the art of painting the forehead with the mark; the word *Visesaka* itself means the *tilak* on the forehead. Thin and tender Bhujrja, leaves were cut into different patterns and used on the forehead, besides sandalwood, turmeric, *kasturi* (musk), vermilion paste. The art of drawing intricate patterns on the forehead has retained its fascination to the present day. Apart from the forehead other body parts like the chin, neck, palm, breasts were also painted. *Alta* (red colour) was applied on the hands and feet as was *mehendi* (henna), a tradition that has survived till today. Henna was applied on the hands especially of brides as the red colour imparted was considered to be auspicious because of its emotional, sexual and fertility-related qualities.

Gandha-Yukti

The use of perfumes is extremely ancient in India extolled even in the scriptures. Details of the manufacturing processes of perfumes appear in a very well-known text as the *Vrihatsamhita* written by Varahamihira. Cosmetics, perfumes, deodorants, perfumed hair-oil, body creams, room fresheners, *agarbatis* and *dhoop* (incense) were made and used in copious quantities. It has been said that there were almost one lakh seventy-four thousand seven hundred and twenty methods for manufacturing perfumes. Rose water, sandalwood paste, musk, floral extracts like jasmine, rose, *champa* (frangipani), were all mixed and used imaginatively resulting in a bewildering array of fragrances.

Dassanavasanangaraga

Besides external ornamentation, the *Kama Sutra* also addresses the need for personal hygiene. Although this dwells on decorating the teeth, there was an equal emphasis on keeping them clean and sweet smelling at all times. The art itself was centered on painting the teeth, usually in gold or silver colours. Panini, the grammarian, makes a distinction between *Dantalekhaka* who is a painter of teeth and *Nakhalekhaka*, a painter of nails. There are three divisions within this art, all of which centres around the use of colour— painting, dyeing and using colour on the face.

The second subdivision was known as *Vasanaraga* or the art of dyeing clothes, making coloured borders and printing floral impressions as well as embroidery work.

The third subdivision *Angaraga* was the use of colour for toiletry and make-up. Before the advent of designer creams were the days of cosmetics derived from natural sources—lac mixed with castor oil was used to paint lips, a fine powder called *lodhra-renu* was used on the face, lamp black used as kohl to outline the eyes, a mixture of gram powder, sandalwood powder and turmeric was used all over the body for cleansing. Some books talk about the technique of using a light *Alaktaka* colour on the lip and then rubbing it with *Sikthaka gutika* or candle wax balls, which would heighten the colour and make the lips shine.

The *Kama Sutra* deals extensively with the use of various methods prevalent then. Oils like almond, coconut *til* oil were used all over the body and on the hair to keep it

black, shiny and long. Creams including butter-based ones were used all over the body to keep the skin soft and supple. The purpose of *Angaraga* is not merely indulgence. The Ayurveda texts too believed that if the limbs and other parts of the body were properly rubbed down and cleansed, the body remained healthy and a sense of well being kept diseases at bay.

Vastragopana

This relates to the important art of couture. Wearing clothes well, developing a style, and improvisation are all discussed here. The text looks at how to wear clothes properly so that they do not slip off, to improvise when new clothes are not available so that one always looks well dressed, and to wear even an ill fitting dress as a fitting one.

Abhushana Alankara

The meaning of *bhushana* is to adorn and *abhushan* means ornaments meant to adorn. Looking good enhanced a good physique that was further enhanced by wearing *abhushan* or ornaments. According to ancient texts there were specific scientific reasons to wear ornaments and they affected the physical and mental well being of a person. Silver was believed to be a cold metal and used to calm down an angry or agitated mind, whereas gold was considered to be hot, energizing a person besides ensuring ceremonial purity. So it was believed that the use of these metals reduced the risk of cancer and balanced blood circulation. So Indians continue to revel in wearing jewellery and no part of the body is left unadorned. Earrings, finger rings in all five fingers, toe rings, anklets, bangles, hair ornaments, ornaments that were worn on the parting of the hair, waist bands, forearm bands, nose rings, all made out of pearls, precious gems, gold and silver were de rigueur. Ancient Indians mastered the art of studying gems and their effects on various ailments and temperaments. Astrologers too advised the use of gems to ward off the effects of planetary disturbances.

Kesha Samskara

Kesha samskara deals with the art of hairdressing. Long hair was seen as an *abhushan* or ornament enhancing the beauty of a woman. Elaborate hairstyles were devised as seen in the frescoes of Ajanta and Ellora and the sculptures of Belur and Halebid. Added to the hairstyles were ornaments that besides keeping the hair in place added to their allure.

The *Nava Rasas*, the sixty four arts, the science of *Kama Shastras* were all to be understood and assimilated if one wanted to be a good lover and a good spouse. The use of these arts was considered imperative to woo and attract an accomplished partner. Yet if these did not work and one failed to attract the attention of a suitable mate, there was still no cause for despair as the *Kama Sutra* had remedies for this too.

Good looks, good qualities, health, youth, and liberality are the chief and most natural means of making a person agreeable in the eyes of others. However, when a person fails to obtain the object of his desires, the text says, 'a man or a woman should resort to artificial means and the following are some recipes that may be found useful.' Combining Ayurveda and alchemy, these recipes enumerated in the *Kama Sutra* explain in detail methods for enhancing beauty, magic mantras to attract men, hymns for seducing women, amongst other things. Some of them are indeed rather extreme but then desperate needs demand desperate measures.

Cosmetics

An ointment made of the *tabernamontana coronaria*, the *costus speciosus* or *arabicus*, and the *flacourtia cataphracta*, can be used as an unguent of adornment. If a fine powder is made of the above plants, and applied to the wick of a lamp, which is made to burn with the oil of blue vitrol, the black pigment or lamp black thus produced, when applied to the eyelashes, has the effect of making a person look lovely. The oil of the hogweed, the *echites putescens*, the sarina plant, the yellow amaranth, and the leaf of the nymphae, if applied to the body, has the same effect. The black pigment from the same plants produces a similar effect.

If the bone of a camel is dipped into the juice of the plant *eclipta prostata*, and then burnt, and the black pigment produced from its ashes is placed in a box also made of the bone of a camel, and applied together with antimony to the eye lashes with a pencil also made of the bone of a camel, then that pigment is said to be very pure, and wholesome for the eyes, and serves as a means of subjugating others to the person who uses it. The same effect can be produced by black pigment made of the bones of hawks, vultures, and peacocks.

Attracting Women

Eating the powder of the *nelumbrium speciosum*, the blue lotus, and the *mesna roxburghii*, with ghee and honey, makes a man attractive. If the bone of a peacock or a hyena is covered with gold, and tied on the right hand, it makes a man attractive in the eyes of other people. In the same way, if a bead made of the seed of the jujube, or a conch shell, is enchanted by the incantations of those well skilled in the science of magic, and tied on the hand, it produces the same result.

The remains of a kite who has died a natural death, ground into powder, and mixed with cowach and honey, has also the same effect. Anointing oneself with an ointment made of the plant *emblica myrabolans* has the power of subjecting women to one's will. By burning these sprouts at night and looking at the smoke, if he sees a golden moon behind, he will then be successful with any woman; or if he throws some of the powder of these same sprouts mixed with the excrement of a monkey upon a maiden, she will not be given in marriage to anybody else.

Subjugation of Women

If pieces of the arris root are dressed with the oil of the mango, and placed for six months in a hole made in the trunk of the Sisu tree, and are then taken out and made into an ointment, and applied to the penis, this is said to serve as the means of subjugating women.

Benefits from these Arts

The aesthetics of eroticism is an integral part of Indian sensibilities, *Kama* having been one of the first to rise from the primordial chaos. Its interplay has commandeered the laws of society, art, literature and the principles of living for centuries. Aesthetics apart, there were other practical benefits as well: it helped enhance beauty, built character and self-confidence and also defined the virtues of a woman. Besides men and women who were proficient were honoured by kings, praised by the cognoscenti and were showered with money, gifts and honours. Princesses and noblewomen were able to gain control over their husbands and ensure that they stayed faithful. Widows and women whose husbands travelled had no difficulty finding lovers, if they mastered these arts. Gifted courtesans were the toast of the town, celebrated denizens who gained the respect of society. Thus an accomplished person was automatically recognized and given a place of honour in society. Most importantly, these arts gave mankind a channel for self-expression and seeking fulfilment—they made it possible to experience ecstasy.

The Principles of Pleasure
Foreplay

A woman being of a tender nature wants
tender beginnings…The rules of the Shastra
apply so long as passion is moderate but
when the wheel of love is set in motion,
there is then no Shastra and no order…

A lingering glance, the flutter of the eyelids, or the unspoken word—all these carry a far more powerful message of sensuality than the physical act of intercourse. An affectionate touch or a tender caress often speaks louder than a thousand words. Even though we live in an era that is not known for its subtlety of expression, where permissiveness, nudity and overt promiscuity have conspired to effectively erase the ideal of romance, there is a persistent yearning for a bygone era where grace and sensuousness were the mainstay of every relationship, where lovers delighted in the fragrance of jasmine flowers, the melody of songbirds, a touch and the ritual of seduction that presaged lovemaking. The wisdom of the *Kama Sutra* is more relevant today than ever before, for it lays great emphasis on mastering the game of flirtation and the need to understand the nuances of foreplay as a prelude to sexual gratification.

As with everything else, foreplay begins with desire in the mind when it first contemplates physical intimacy with a loved one. Desire encompasses the entire pattern of behaviour, the building up of stimuli that lead up to orgasm for mutual gratification. Undressing, kissing, petting, flirting, oral sex, cuddling are all-important especially for women who need prolonged stimulation in order to reach complete arousal. Ultimately good sex is about attentiveness, being sensitive to the partner's needs and the desire to ensure that the experience is intensely pleasurable and memorable for both.

Traditionally, foreplay was considered to be something that a man did to woo and seduce his partner. Today, foreplay has become an integral part of the whole sexual experience. So many women readily agree that physical affection is a more significant expression of intimacy than sex. Although an unplanned sexual encounter can sometimes be a startlingly sensuous experience, in general, most women believe and agree that good sex must necessarily include prolonged foreplay.

Human males are no exception to the mating patterns that are seen in nature and as with every other species, it takes a persistent man to track, persuade and coax a woman to have intercourse with him. Men have the added responsibility to ensure that the woman too is satisfied and that the encounter can turn into a relationship.

Kama Sutra *on Wooing*

Desire is what drives and motivates men and women to seek out one another and yearn for closer contact. With this in mind, the *Kama Sutra* sets about explaining the ways and means by which to woo and win women. The text advises a young man to spend time with the girl, amuse her with games and diversions, cook, play cards and dice with her, her friends and confidants. Thereafter he should ply her with gifts of jewellery and flowers. The next step in the wooing game is one of persuasion, to get her to meet him privately. As Vatsyayana states, 'Because they belong to the same species, man and woman seek the same pleasure in sexual relations. This is why desire must first be stimulated by preliminary attentions.'

First impressions have a habit of becoming lasting ideas, therefore correct behaviour, demeanour, attention to dressing, hygiene, a genuine interest in pleasuring the woman are prerequisites not merely for seduction but for any enduring relationship. The man should ensure that he is well groomed, cleanly attired and makes a good impression, for women like men who are physically attractive. The wooing moreover has to continue well after the initial flush of love has been consummated. Great skill is required to keep the fire of love burning and recapture the romance and excitement of the early days especially for couples that have been in long-term relationships. Most forget the thrill of flirting and the excitement of courtship. Therefore, says the *Kama Sutra*, wooing is a lesson for a lifetime, to be learnt and re-defined at various stages of every relationship.

Facing page: *All activities of the senses require continuous practice in order to manifest themselves; love too is born of long practice like the love of hunting for the hunter.*

Signs and Gestures

In these days of sexual aggression, the notion of a woman having to express desire with a glance may appear outmoded but many still thrill at a tacit glance, an inviting gesture. Reading body language is an art that has never died and to correctly interpret desire is indeed a skill that has to be acquired. The woman who wants to respond to the man does so, according to the *Kama Sutra* not overtly but with signs and gestures. The message that she sends out is implicit but without ambiguity: she looks at him shyly with her head half bent, seeks any pretext to touch him, is incoherent when he addresses her, delights in his company, converses with him for a long time on trivial matters, plays with the ringlets in her hair, avoids being seen by her lover when she is not dressed and made up, always wears anything that he presents her. 'A man, who has seen and perceived the feelings of the girl towards him, and who has noticed the outward signs and movements by which those feelings are expressed, should do everything in his power to seek union with her.'

Setting the Mood

Setting the scene and creating the right environment and mood is an essential component of the sensual art of making love. With its intimate understanding of human desire, the *Kama Sutra* says: 'A woman being of a tender nature wants tender beginnings.' A tender word to assuage her fears, an intimate touch to heighten desire, a glass of wine to help shed inhibitions are all part of the recommended sixty-four ways through which passion can culminate in successful union. These sixty-four ways constitute the foreplay that precedes actual lovemaking: the *Kama Sutra* classifies all manner of embraces, kisses, and touching, biting. Lessons on how to take clothes off, the creative use of imagination and fantasy, the switching of roles etc., are but a few pointers. Furthermore, it gives detailed instructions on how to mold foreplay to suit the differing temperaments of one's lover.

The ancient text placed strong emphasis on teaching a man to place a woman's pleasure before his own. It is an accepted fact that women get aroused more slowly than men and although there are exceptions to every rule, an average woman doesn't get enough foreplay. However passionate a man, if he initiates intercourse before the woman is completely ready, it will invariably lead to discontentment and unhappiness. Inevitably too, intercourse where there is no mutual desire, lasts only a few minutes. The *Kama Sutra* understandably issues a warning: 'One thing certain is that a man whose activity lasts long pleases a woman, while on the other hand they [women] complain of men who reach orgasm rapidly.' Therefore, penetration should not be done until the woman is fully aroused. Modern research states that whereas it takes an average man ten minutes to get ready for sexual intercourse, the average woman may take anything between 25 to 40 minutes to reach a state of arousal. This makes it all the more evident why the *Kama Sutra* so thoroughly addressed the need for multiple forms of love play.

Facing page: *A man who has seen and perceived the feelings of the girl, and noticed the outward signs and gestures, should do everything in his power to seek union with her.*

63

Intimate contact with a woman falls into two categories—external and internal. External contact involves fondling, caressing, kissing, touching and so on. With increasing intimacy, an external contact is converted into an internal one during which no barriers exist between man and woman. However, external contact need not necessarily always lead to sex. Most women say that they prefer intimacy to the actual sexual act: kissing, embracing, talking—all these take precedence over the act itself as they portray a caring man interested in the woman rather than in instant gratification. Men, on the other hand, believe that foreplay is a prelude to intercourse and is juvenile unless it culminates in physicality. Men's egos come into play, as they believe that it is size and stamina that sustains desire. These differences often lead women to refuse many a man any intimacy fearing that sex would then be mandatory. The very modern *Kama Sutra* guides a man to enjoy a woman sensually and erotically, without intercourse. Most couples have varying needs; few are turned on simultaneously or precisely when the partner wants sex. While the physical act can be the ultimate physical manifestation of desire, closeness and bonding between couples usually comes from intimacy that becomes an expression of a deeper love and understanding. It is imperative to build up closeness throughout the day in order to enjoy a night filled with passion.

Vatsyayana was right in assuming that sexuality begins in the mind and that the right manner to win over a loved one was to first create chemistry. All the five sense organs should thus come into play to create a heightened sense of passion: pleasurable sights, aromatic smells, sensuously touching and kissing, melodious music, delectable food and drink for the palate.

Erotic Touching

Tactility or touching is key in communicating desire. The entire body is responsive to touch and touching provides a wonderful opportunity to explore the body's erogenous zones. Touching 'by accident' can have an extraordinary effect; some *Kama Shastra* texts talk about how the hair on the arm stands on end, when the woman fleetingly touches a man. To prolong these magical moments, the *Kama Sutra* says that a woman's body is full of erogenous zones and advises engaging the entire body in sensual play: to kiss, touch and worship not just the genital area but the fingers, arms, legs as well as the back, leisurely unravelling the sensual mysteries of her body. Besides the hand, the tongue too can play a vital role in the game of arousal. Licking with the tongue and exploring the entire length of each other's bodies can be a delicious form of foreplay. Fingers too can be used creatively in adventurous pleasuring: caressing the different parts of the body, kissing the hand tenderly, massaging the body with aromatic oils are all highly erotic. Exploring the vagina with the fingers is also an intimate form of foreplay.

Other forms of touching include stroking, caressing and holding, kissing, nibbling, sucking and licking. The sweep of a woman's hair, the soft brush against erect nipples and even the warmth of the breath can be truly arousing sensations.

Embracing

Embracing brings together two people who have until then been apart. Embracing can be of two kinds depending on whether the partners know each other or are strangers. Between lovers who are already aroused, an embrace can be charged with passion while with shy or embarrassed lovers, embracing removes physical distance and establishes intimacy. It is said that there are four distinct stages in the process of embracing—touching, pulling, rubbing and pressing hard. First the partners touch each other lovingly while talking. In the next stage they step closer. Once

Blinded by desire, unable to wait, they press against each other with the same passion, face to face, whether seated or lying down.

their bodies come into contact, the lovers begin to touch, caress and stroke each other and as desire mounts, both press hard against each other as a prelude to intercourse.

The *Kama Sutra* has many an advice to offer. For example, if the girl is an adult or if the man has known her for some time, he may embrace her by the light of a lamp, but if she is very young or if he is not well acquainted with her, he should embrace her in darkness. When the girl accepts the embrace, the man should put a *tambula* (betel leaf) into her mouth, and if she repulses him, he should cajole her with conciliatory words, entreaties and even kneel at her feet.

Once the girl is ready and willing, the *Kama Sutra* defines different types of embraces:

Jataveshtitaka, or the twining of a creeper
When a woman, clinging to a man as a creeper twines round a tree, bends her head while slightly making the sound 'sut sut' embraces him, it is called an embrace like the 'twining of a creeper'.

Vrikshadhirudhaka, or climbing a tree
When a woman, having placed one of her feet on the foot of her lover, and the other on one of his thighs, passes one of her arms around his back, and the other on his shoulders, as if she is climbing him in order to have a kiss, such an embrace is called the 'climbing of a tree'.

Tila-Tandulaka, or the mixture of sesame seed with rice
When lovers lying on a bed embrace each other so closely that the arms and thighs of the one are encircled by the arms and thighs of the other, and are, as it were, rubbing up against them, this is called an embrace like 'the mixture of sesame seed with rice'.

Kshiraniraka, or milk and water embrace
When a man and a woman are very much in love with each other, and, immuned to pain or hurt, embrace each other as if they were entering into each other's bodies either while the woman is sitting on the lap of the man, in front of him, or on a bed, then it is called an embrace like a 'mixture of milk and water'.

Facing page: Assured and showing off her beauty she encircles her lover like a liana around a sal tree; bending her face towards him for a kiss she withdraws with a small sigh.

In all there are eight kinds of embraces with four additional ones like the embrace of the thighs, the embrace of the *Jaghana*, that is, the part of the body from the navel downwards to the thighs, the embrace of the breasts and the embrace of the forehead in which the lovers touch the mouth, eyes and the forehead of the other with their own.

The whole subject of embracing is such even hearing or talking about it will infuse a desire for enjoyment. Even those embraces that are not mentioned in the *Kama Shastra* should be practised if they are conducive to the increase of passion. The rules of the *Shastra* apply so long as passion is moderate but when the wheel of love is set in motion, there is then no Shastras and no order.

Kissing

Face-to-face gazing into each other's eyes, their brows joint, the one against the other, immediately arouses ardour.

There is nothing more intimate than a kiss, for kissing is an expression of intimacy, willingness and mutual desire. Kissing is the best form of

foreplay and may accompany an embrace or follow it. Kissing can have varying grades of intensity, whereby the lips and tongue can be used imaginatively. The *Kama Sutra* offers a wide range of advice about the varieties and manners of kissing. It says that there are seven areas in a woman's body that are extremely sensitive to kissing: the forehead, cheeks, eyes, breasts, nipples, lips, and the vulva. Before delving into the techniques, Vatsyayana offers some rather mundane but essential guidance:

Clean breath

Nothing can be more off putting than bad breath, so the text recommends that lovers should ensure that teeth are clean and brushed and nothing overtly strong smelling be eaten before kissing. It advocates the use of mouth fresheners like mint before embracing the lover.

Position

The partners while kissing should ensure that no encumbrances come in the way of close contact. When they come close, they should tilt the

Passion and respect arise in a man who sees from a distance a young girl with the marks of nails cut into her breasts.

69

।।कोयराहैखभावइसी।।थारा अधररोभ्रकतस्त्रीएदे।।नेलोहेजीवाउ।। कोसीभां
ध दसेथ के था रे विषसन भारोच्यो है।।हेराधेनारायएवतेंद्रतुसरा।।

।।७५

head slightly to an angle, to avoid collision. To this end, a soft preliminary touching of the lips makes for a good beginning.

Closed eyes

In most instances, women tend to close their eyes before kissing, although kissing with open eyes and looking into one another's eyes can be very erotic.

Open lips

Vatsyayana recommends that the lips should be slightly parted, moist and prepared for the lover. Initially the lips should be just pressed together and then the pressure can increase or the tongue used to run over the lips in a circular motion. On the other hand, lips that are chapped or pursed together, are not open and welcoming are an indication that the partner is displeased or not willing to go any further. Similarly, a turning away of the head and offering the cheek for a kiss is another indication of displeasure or anger.

Using the hands and body

There are many ways to use the hand while kissing—usually one hand goes around the waist and the other one against the middle of the back. Other ways are to cup the lover's face, place the hands around the neck, encircle the waist, and hold the head with one hand while caressing the hair. It is painful to hold the lover's neck to steady the body, press too hard while leaning against a wall or door, roughly pull the hair, or hold the arms too tightly.

The *Kama Sutra* also describes different styles of kissing:

A Bent Kiss

'When the heads of two lovers are bent toward each other, and when so bent, kissing takes place.'

The Pressed Kiss
'When a lover presses the lower lips with force, this is known as the pressed kiss.'

The Straight Kiss
'When the lips of two lovers are brought directly to each other, this is called a straight kiss.'

The Clasping Kiss
When the man or the woman 'takes both the lips of the other between his or her own, it is called the clasping kiss'. The *Kama Sutra* goes on to say, 'A woman only takes this kind of kiss from a man with no moustache.' If while kissing, one of them touches the teeth, the tongue, and the palate of the other with his or her tongue, it is called the fighting of the tongue.

The Kiss that Kindles Love
This is a kind of kiss that a woman uses to wake her lover when she wants to make love. 'When a woman looks at the face of her lover while he is asleep and kisses it to show her desire it is called the kiss that kindles love.'

The Awakening Kiss
When a lover coming home late at night and kisses his beloved who is asleep in order to show his desire, it is called a kiss that awakens.

The Turning Away Kiss
When a woman kisses her lover when he is preoccupied with work or something else so that his attention may be diverted, it is called the kiss that turns away.

The Sucking Kiss
This is a very seductive type of kiss. Instead of kissing with the mouth open, suck the lower or upper lip of the partner with your own lips.

Kisses should be placed on the brow, the cheeks, the throat, the eyes, the chest, a woman's breasts, the lower lip and inside the mouth.

Lip Kissing

This too is highly seductive with a surprise element to it. While kissing your lover, gently bite the lip, not too hard to bruise the lips and leave marks, just gently so as not to shock the partner.

A Surprise Kiss

Catching the lover unawares when he is busy, occupied, working or even asleep, place a very gently seductive kiss on his lips. This will immediately draw his attention towards you.

Vacuum Kissing

This is a playful and flirtatious kiss. While kissing with an open mouth, suck the air from your partner's mouth deeply. It is pleasurable and surprising!

Butterfly Kissing

Put your eye close to your lover's cheek and flutter your eyelashes upon his skin. You can also do this on the lips, and even on the penis.

Nail Marks

While kissing kindles the fire of love, scratching with nails acts likes a fuel to keep the fire burning. Nails, however, should be used only when both partners have attained the requisite degree of excitement. Those who lack intensity in love, do not use nails to excite their partners for this will cause pain and can put off the lover. Nails, like kisses, can be used on the armpits, breasts, neck, back, thighs, vagina but care must be taken not to inflict lasting or painful marks. Nails marks are a constant reminder of a night of passion and in fact men as well as women in ancient India grew their nails specifically for the purpose of leaving scratch marks on their lovers. The *Kama Sutra* goes to great lengths about how to leave different-shaped marks as a sign of sexual prowess.

Biting

Biting either accompanies or follows the scratching with nails and adds to the intensity of passion. All the places that can be kissed can also be bitten with the exception of the upper lip, tongue and eyes. Biting must be done in a manner so as not to leave a permanent mark. The neck, armpits and thighs are ideal places for biting though some believe nibbling at the breast to be the most exciting.

Hitting and Sibilating

While hitting may seem rather archaic and barbaric today most *Kama Shastra* texts recommend both of them. Hitting the partner and simultaneously making sibilating sounds are believed to be explicit ways of showing the level of excitement. Men and women can hit their partners on the hand, shoulders, chest, thighs and sides of the body with their fists, palms and fingers. Although the *Kama Sutra* does touch upon it, Vatsyayana is of the opinion that hitting a partner during intercourse is cruel and to be avoided. Sibilation usually accompanies hitting, where sounds, like hissing and sighing, are produced.

Actions of a Man

Undressing a partner

Undressing a lover can become a highly erotic form of foreplay. Undressing begins with undoing of the fastener when the woman usually goes through the motions of protesting any further action. This reluctance and inhibition is shed as passion mounts. Thus, slowly undressing his lady, a man must demonstrate his readiness by touching and stroking sensitive areas like the breasts and nipples.

The first intercourse

The intimacy of intercourse, especially the first time is a private and sensitive moment, to be savoured and cherished through life. Several

ancient Indian texts like the *Grha Shastras* besides the *Kama Sutra* paid great attention to the rituals associated with the wedding, the nuptial night and the appropriate chamber. More than any other time the ambience here has to be perfect as well as seductive: a well-made bed with soft clean sheets and cushions, decorated with scented flowers, perfumed with incense sticks, bodies anointed with scented oils and fragrant with sandalwood paste, saffron and jasmine flowers.

As to the actual method of approaching a woman, the *Kama Sutra* says that the man on entering the room, should occupy a place at the right-hand side of his new bride, and stroking her hair talk gently to her. He should hold and caress her hands. As he approaches the moment to actual intercourse, he should slowly begin to excite the woman by cupping her breasts, kissing the nipples, even as his hands travel down to her thighs and groin area. If a woman is aroused, she will respond by loosening up but if she has never before been with a man, winning her confidence is crucial. Talking, kissing and reassurance is the best way followed by gentle caresses and fondling her erogenous zones, so that she automatically opens up her body to further foreplay. When a man is with a virgin, it is imperative that he understands her sentiments and fears and is watchful of her natural responses.

Most of the texts mentioned above believed in building up expectations and passion by abstinence and a wait to consummate the marriage for at least a three day period, some even recommend that the groom not speak to his bride for those three days. But the followers of Babhravya eschewed this in the belief that if the man did not speak to his new bride she would become dejected and discouraged believing him to be a eunuch.

Vatsyayana himself was of the belief that soon after the wedding, the man should attempt to win the confidence of his bride but abstain at first from sexual contact. He believed that women should be gently initiated into the pleasures of sex because if men who are virtual strangers forcibly approach them, they sometimes became haters of sex as well as men. So he recommends that the man should create confidence in the girl and then on the second and third nights, he should feel her whole body with his hands, kiss her all over, touch her vagina, loosen her girdle and the knot of her dress and at last, after having

Facing page: A woman is like a flower; she must be treated gently until she feels secure. If she is violently assaulted she becomes hostile to any sign of affection. One must therefore strive to pacify her.

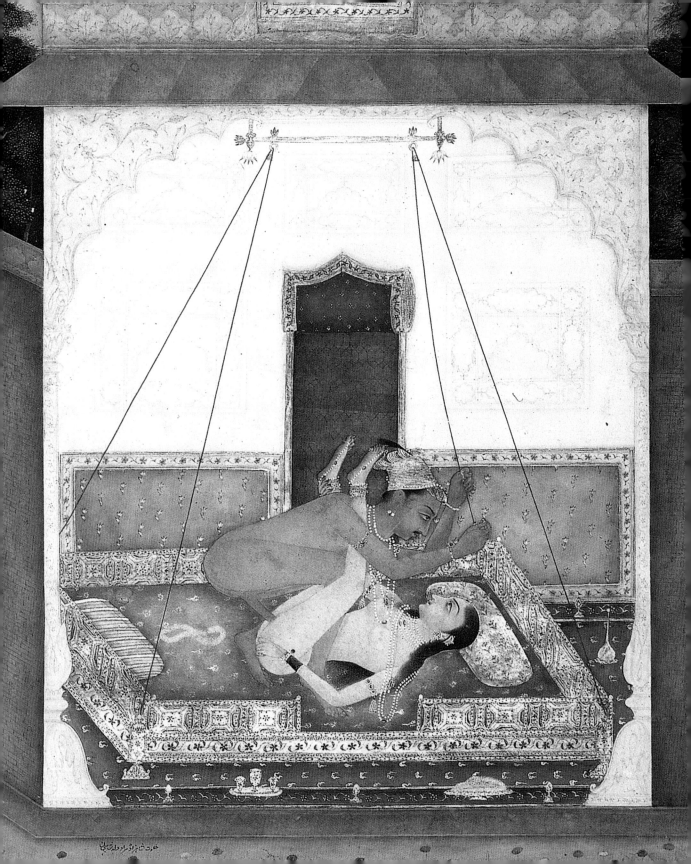

overcome her bashfulness, he should enjoy her in a way so as not to frighten her.

The idea of abstinence was based on ancient Hindu beliefs that deferring sex would heighten passion, and accumulating semen for procreation was the primary goal of intercourse, especially in marriage. It was also recommended because women were known to have larger sexual appetites and the capacity for multiple orgasms and hence more sexual energy. The man on the other hand, 'once he ejaculates looses interest in sex, totally drained of all desire'. Therefore, it was suggested that a man strive to bring a woman to many orgasms and delay his own.

Foreplay after Intercourse

Some of the most precious moments in a relationship come soon after making love. The *Kama Sutra* reminds us that it is impolite to sleep too soon:

> Those things that increase passion should be done first, and those for amusement should be done afterward.

It recommends embracing and kissing after intercourse, and after cleaning and bathing spending time with each other by talking, playing games, drinking and partaking of good foods. In short, Vatsyayana recommends that the ideal of romance be maintained throughout the game of love. Be it in sighting a lover, wooing and winning the lover leading right up to the act of intercourse, grace and etiquette coupled with passion and experience are pathways to ecstasy. There is a catch though: these are qualities that have to be pursued with relentless patience and persistence.

Facing page: *When the couple is free from desire, they should seat themselves comfortably and intimately rub each other with sandalwood paste.*

Arousing Ardour Postures

Women love the man whose sexual energy lasts a long time, but they resent a man whose energy ends quickly because he stops before they reach a climax…

*T*he *Kama Sutra* is best known for those chapters that describe in vivid detail the various postures or positions for intercourse. These were not merely yogic contortions but based on scientific classifications that analyzed which partner would be best suited for maximizing pleasure. Twenty centuries ago, Vatsyayana had come to the very sophisticated conclusion that unequal partnerships lead to unfulfilled passions. These, in turn, lead to unhappiness and discontentment. When sex is no more than an outcome of habit and proximity, it produces distaste and displeasure. When langour sets in and couples get complacent, what is needed is imagination and effort to recreate romantic connections if the frisson of sexuality is to be rekindled. Expanding sensual connections needs personal maturity, attentiveness and disciplining the mind as much as it requires the disciplining of the body.

The solution, says Vatsyayana, lies in striking the right balance between all the human urges: physical, emotional, intellectual, social, sexual and spiritual. Compatibility was the key to true pleasure, so partners must suit each other in every respect: be it in temperament, the extent of passion, their physique, even the size of their genital organs. With a comprehensive understanding of inter-personal relationships, the *Kama Sutra* offers very urbane insights for satisfactory sex and ways to overcome tedium: 'The chief reason for the separation between husband and wife; the cause that drives the husband to the embraces of strange women and the wife to the arms of strange men is the want for varied pleasures and the monotony that follows possession. Monotony begets satiety and satiety (begets) distaste for congress and soon one or the other yields to temptation. It seldom happens that the two love each other equally therefore the one is more easily seduced by passion than

the other. The first consideration for a satisfactory sex life is that coition should be attempted only when both parties are inclined towards it; the second consideration is that intercourse should be preceded by such acts of love as would stimulate both partners equally. The third consideration is that the act should be undertaken in a posture, which would give maximum amount of pleasure and satisfaction. The posture adapted should be constantly varied to prevent monotony and preferences should be given to those postures where maximum mutual caresses are possible.'

Variations in the place of making love, in postures, in style, surroundings were all considered necessary to combat monotony. The *Kama Sutra*, therefore, goes into great detail about creating the right ambience and setting for making love. Variety apart, compatibility is the key ingredient needed for sustaining long-term relationships as well-matched couples maximize coordination of their efforts for mutual satisfaction. Vatsyayana was acutely aware that the physiology of men and women was different and that while it took a very short time for a man to orgasm, women took much longer to climax. Therefore, other

Variations in the place of making love, in the styles and surroundings are all important to combat monotony.

things being equal, it becomes important that the genital organ sizes of the couples match. When they did it becomes important to pay attention not merely prolonging intercourse but to ensure that women are in positions that made it possible for them to experience orgasm along with their partners.

With the typical proclivity that existed in ancient India for classification and compartmentalization, Vatsyayana divided men and women into divisions in much the same way that natural history classified the animal world. Women were categorized according to their physical attributes, temperament, moods and the depth of their vaginas, whereas men were classified according to the size of their penises. Just as Greeks considered Venus as the epitome of beauty, Indians considered Padmini or the Lotus Woman as the most perfect representative of the feminine form. Such a woman had a face like the full moon; her body was as soft as a mustard flower, her skin as fine, tender and fair as the yellow lotus, her eyes as bright and beautiful as those of a fawn, her full bosom rounded, hard and high, and she had three folds of skin around her navel.

Lovemaking should be undertaken in postures that maximize pleasure and satisfaction.

Similar descriptions detail the other categories of women: *Chitrini* or the Art Woman and *Shankhini* or the Conch Woman. According to the size and depth of their vaginas, they were classified as *Mrigi* (doe-like), *Badava* (cow-like) or *Hastini* (like a she-elephant). Men, on the other hand, are classified according to the size and depth of their penises into *Shash* or the Rabbit Man who has a small phallus, *Vrish*, the Bull Man, who has a normal-sized organ and the *Ashva* or the Horse man who has an extremely large phallus. The endeavour was to find the right match, for example a union of a *Shashak* (rabbit) Male with a *Mrigi* (doe) woman, of a *Vrish* (bull) male with a *Badava* (cow) woman and a *Ashva* (horse) male with a *Hastini* (she-elephant) woman was considered to be well matched because the sizes of their genital organs would be equal to one another.

According to the *Kama Sutra*, there are six different kinds of unmatched union. The text however provides solutions for these mismatched couples. When there is disparity in the sizes of the male and female organs it advises certain positions that favour better adaptation. For example, if the penis is disproportionately large or when the woman is very young certain postures are to be avoided to prevent pain and injury. Some postures stimulate desire in both partners while others give no satisfaction at all, especially to women. Some positions increase the chances of conception, while others lessen it; other postures are harmful during pregnancy.

Besides these detailed descriptions, Vatsyayana further classified men and women based on their suitability to have sex. Spinsters, widows who had remarried, and prostitutes were considered fit for sex and he classified them as *Gamya*. Those who were not fit for a physical relationship, he called *Agamya* partners. Amongst these were lepers, those who were insane, corrupt, those without character and snitches. He further elaborates that women who want to make love with all the lights on are stingy, and those past their prime and extremely fair-skinned are also not fit for intercourse. He asserts that one must not strive to establish physical relations with an ascetic woman, a friend of the wife, a friend's wife, a teacher and the wife of the king.

In addition to this, males had to be gentlemen…but who actually qualified to be called a gentleman? Vatsyayana says that a legitimate wife,

Facing page: 'O Supreme Being! Stimulate the seed that I pour into this woman today. In order to fulfill my desire, she will spread her thighs so that my rod inspired by desire penetrates her vagina.'

proper occupation and financial well-being are pre-requisites for a civilized man. Equally important—if both partners want to enjoy intimacy—is a strong, healthy body. The postures recommended in the text were derived from Patanjali's famous *Yoga Shastras* and were meant not merely to keep the body supple but also to develop the mind. These *asanas* were 'attitudes' designed to make the body strong and flexible—balanced and graceful—healthy and fit as well as increase the body's reservoir of energy. The *asanas* also helped women heal minor disorders and ensured that they did not suffer from menstrual or menopausal problems, or complications related to pregnancy or childbirth. Besides this, the text also lays great emphasis on personal hygiene and recommends that a cultured man should live in a conducive surrounding that is clean, well maintained and near a water body. Great attention too, he advises, has to be paid to the bed on which love is to be made—it should be comfortable, and have soft cushions with clean, white sheets.

As far as women's sexuality is concerned, the *Kama Sutra* is extremely modern in its outlook. While many women even today believe that their main role in a relationship is to please and pleasure the man, leaving

By paying attention to the needs of his wife, and varying the manner of making love, a husband can enjoy sex with her as if with thirty-two different women.

behind their own needs, Vatsyayana pays special attention to the fulfilment of the sexual needs of women. Around the 4th century AD, when the *Kama Sutra* was written, women, unbound by conventional norms of contemporary society, had the liberty and freedom to exercise their options when it came to sexuality. The *Kama Sutra* thus emphasizes the need for a woman to have an intimate knowledge of her body as well as her sexual needs as she can then guide her man without inhibition. The text encourages women to reverse roles, take the initiative while making love, assume the position on top and control the tempo of love making. The text however cautions that just as a woman needs to seek her fulfilment she should also be attuned to the needs and moods of the man if mutual satisfaction and orgasm has to be achieved.

The man too, in turn, has to be attentive and should always make a point of pressing those parts of a woman's body to which she turns her eyes. The *Kama Sutra* lists the following signs as indications of a woman's enjoyment and satisfaction: her body relaxes she closes her eyes she sets aside all bashfulness and shows an increasing willingness to unite with the man, her hands tremble, she does not want to let go off the man, she feels dejected or she bites. In such cases, the man should caress the vagina of the woman until it is soft and after that should proceed to have intercourse. The *Kama Sutra* thus recognizes women as full, lusty participants in the act of love and exhorts men to learn ejaculatory control to last long enough to bring them to orgasm: 'Women love the man whose sexual energy lasts a long time, but they resent a man whose energy ends quickly because he stops before they reach a climax.'

Fortunately, the ancient love manual offers many suggestions for prolonging the act of intercourse. Besides external aids like potions, creams and aphrodisiacs, Vatsyayana recommends several positions that increase a woman's pleasure and reduce a man's stimulation at the same time. Of particular concern, now as then, was the problem of premature ejaculation. As the *Kama Sutra* states, 'Man experiences pleasure up to ejaculation, while the woman's pleasure is continuous. When he has ejected his semen, he seeks rest, whereas she wishes to continue.' The text recommends that if one is incapable of satisfying sexually aggressive women, a weakened man should resort to the use of yogic techniques.

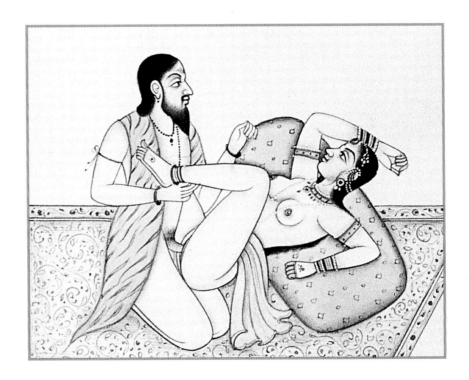

The purpose of these detailed descriptions in the *Kama Sutra* was to ensure that both women and men could understand the complexities involved in intimacy. The *Kama Sutra* thus describes sixty-four postures through which a man and a woman can establish physical contact. Vatsyayana maintains that by paying attention to the needs of his wife and varying the manner of making love a husband can enjoy sex with her as if with thirty-two different women, thus rendering satiety impossible. However, Vatsyayana himself advises caution in attempting some of the postures, for while several of them are basic enough, others are decidedly acrobatic.

Every man and woman knows that more than technique or size what is required for sexual satisfaction is passion. A performance remains just that if acted out without the tenderness and compassion that drives all human emotion: when desire overwhelms the body and spirits soar high, when every caress, touch, eye contact, whisper and position comes alive and is savoured. So, gymnastics in bed is not the end game but rather a means to explore every avenue to enhance the sensations and create new magic every time rather than slip into

boredom and repugnance. The *Kama Sutra* thus opens up a world of sexual choreography and technique that can be learned methodically and from whose knowledge comes new insight—a way to rediscover passion and intimacy.

The Postures

The first step towards intercourse is for the man to ensure that the woman is relaxed, excited, enthusiastic and properly lubricated. There are several manual ways to enhance a woman's level of excitement by kissing, licking, fondling her breasts, scratching, biting and fondling the vagina with the skilful use of fingers. As no two women make love in quite the same manner the man needs to orchestrate his rhythms to suit the moods and temperament of his lover.

The following are the best possible positions classified according to the organ sizes of both men and women:

However virtuous a woman seems, or however sensual she appears, she reveals her true nature in action.

The Kama Sutra describes sixty-four postures through which a man and a woman can establish physical contact. These postures were described at length not to titillate but to educate, as knowledge was considered to be an essential ingredient for fulfillment. Variety was recommended to prevent monotony and to ensure that interest was kept alive in both people. *Ananda* or bliss was the primary objective of physical intimacy and if a couple failed to enjoy intimacy, sex was meaningless. Therefore to ensure that men and women do not lose touch with their desire, to guarantee that the fire of passion burns brightly after many years of marriage, to make certain that both, especially women feel desired and desirable, the *Kama Sutra* recommends breaking out of the routine and monotonous ways of intercourse. Instead it literally opens up innumerable possibilities and variations that make it possible to touch, feel and explore every part of the body—breasts, thighs, hips, eyes, lips, hair in an effort to keep sexuality alive. The *Kama Sutra* thus advises couples to adopt such postures that will help maximize mutual pleasure, result in conception, realize passion and, most importantly, culminate in mutual orgasm.

Mrigi *or the Doe-woman*

Mrigi or the Doe-woman has the following three ways of lying down during intercourse:

The yawning position or widely opened position

When she lowers her head and raises her middle parts, it is called the 'widely opened position'. At such a time the man should apply some unguent, so as to make the entrance easy. When she raises her thighs and keeps them wide apart and engages in intercourse, it is called the 'yawning position'.

The position of the wife of Indra

The woman also known as Indrani draws up both her knees until they nuzzle the curves of her breasts; her feet find support in her lover's armpits. Much has been written on this posture and how to master it. Small girls love this posture, but becoming a goddess like Indrani takes a lot of practice.

Embracing from behind the woman who has her back to him, he turns her around. This requires considerable practice.

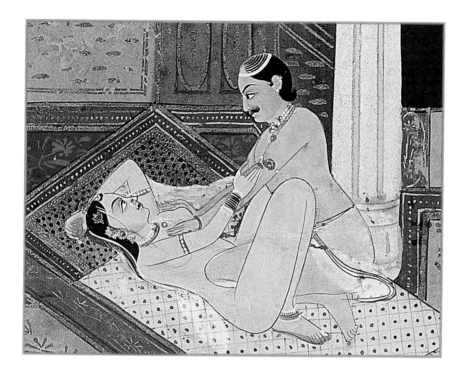

The doe posture

Just as a coy doe spreads both her hind legs to facilitate the entry of the male; similarly a woman with a small and tight vagina spreads her legs wide part. This is regarded as the most civilized of postures and in this position the phallus of even a horse-type of male can make an easy entry.

Hastini *or She-elephant Posture*

This posture is adapted by the *Hastini* or she-elephant, who typically has a large vagina. If her man is small (rabbit type or bull type), such a woman should cuddle beside him and contract herself to the size of her partner.

Samarati *or Equally Matched Unions*

If the male and female partners are well matched with regard to the size of their bodies, they can stretch their bodies naturally for maximum

At nighttime, he approaches her intentionally, kisses her hands and fingers arousing in her the desire for amorous games.

enjoyment. When the legs of both the male and the female are stretched straight out over each other, it is called the 'clasping position'. This has two variations, the side position and the supine position, according to the way in which they lie down. In the side position the male should invariably lie on his left side, and cause the woman to lie on her right side.

Badava Asana *or Cow Posture*

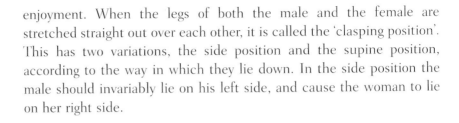

This posture is for women of normal stature. If a cow-type female is having intercourse with an *Ashva* (horse) type male, she must spread her legs as far apart as possible to facilitate the entry of a large phallus. If she is making love with a *Shashak* (rabbit) type male, she should contract her body to the size of her partner. If the partner is of the bull type, then they can spread and stretch their bodies to enjoy union. This type of union is called *Samputak*. This posture is useful when both the partners are well matched. But in any case, women should commence intercourse only when their vaginas have been lubricated thoroughly.

Supine

Lying down supine on the bed is a facilitating posture for the females to enjoy intercourse. In such a posture, folding the knees and raising the thighs up while spreading both the legs apart facilitates an easy entry. In this posture, even a doe-type female can easily be entered by a horse-type male.

Bhugnak

Facing page: Overcome with passion, she caresses him with one hand, with the other arm she arouses him by touching him and massaging him as though by chance.

Here the woman who is lying supine folds her legs at the knees and raises the thighs, but does not spread the legs apart. Instead she rests her knees against the chest of her mate who then enters the female in a half-sitting position.

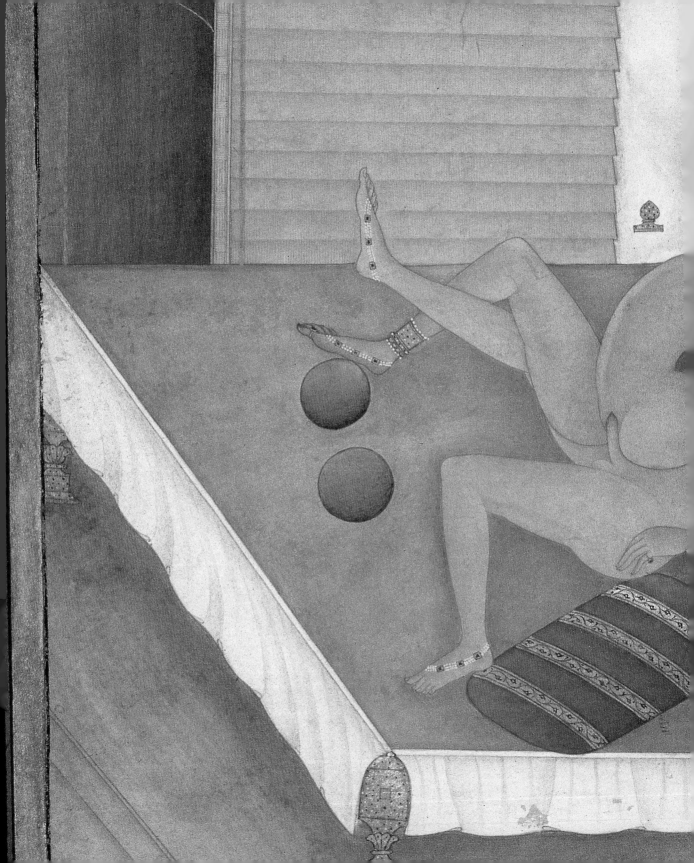

Vadavaka

When, like a mare gripping a stallion, the woman traps and milks the penis with her vagina, it is known as *Vadavaka*. This position that can be ecstatic for the man and very satisfying to the woman is also known as the Mare's Trick and entails rapid contraction and tightening of the vagina. With this posture, a she-elephant type of female can please even a rabbit-type of male who feels as if his penis has been extraordinarily enlarged. This posture can only be perfected with long practice and requires very strong and healthy pelvic muscles.

Jrimbhitaka

Here the lady raises her legs and puts them on the shoulders of the male. The male also takes a sitting posture with his knees up to the level of his partner's shoulders. Such a posture results in the contraction of the female genital organ.

Utpiritaka

Here the woman folds her legs, and rests them against the chest of her lover. The man places his legs around the shoulders of the female. All through the mating, the legs of the woman are supported by the man's chest. Such a posture causes a peculiar thumping sensation in the hearts of both the partners.

Padmasana

Here the woman sits in the yogic posture of the *Padmasana* even while lying supine and raises her thighs without undoing the *asana*. The male reaches his hands through the folds of her legs and holds her shoulders in order to mount on her.

Facing page: Sometimes out of passion, custom and temperament, or when a man is tired, the woman reverses the situation and takes the position of the man on top.

The Wheelbarrow

This is a great position for women as it stimulates the G-spot, and gives her quite a bit of control. This position is also very erotic to the man as he has a bird's-eye view of the lady's gorgeous buttocks and the pelvic freedom to thrust effortlessly. Here the woman is upside down and supports herself comfortably with her head resting on her crossed arms so that they form a pillow. The woman here can move rather freely as she can still move her hips and especially in the modi fied position of one leg up, she can raise that leg higher or lower adjusting the height until the penis makes contact with her G-spot. By holding her legs, hips and ankles the man too gets good control while making love.

Viparita Maithuna *or Reversed Intercourse*

This position is considered to be the most sacred by Vatsyayana. 'When a woman sees that her lover is exhausted by constant congress, without having his desire fulfilled, she should lay him down on his back and act his part.'

When the woman is on top, it allows her to be more in control of the sexual momentum. It also allows her to take the initiative and start with touching, embracing, kissing and all other forms of foreplay. The *Kama Sutra* also instructs that the middle and ring finger held together can reach a woman's G-spot that can be stimulated by rhythmically rubbing it. In addition, men can stimulate their partner's vulva, breasts and other body parts with their hands. Men also find women on top particularly pleasurable because of the added visual stimulation of seeing the body movements. Experiment with different rhythms, tilting the pelvis at different angles while simultaneously kissing, licking and biting the lover's mouth, face, neck and ears.

When she climbs upon you,
the flowers dropping from her tousled hair,

her giggles turning to gasps;
every time she bends to kiss your lips
her nipples pierce your chest.
As her hips begin to churn,
her head, flung back, bobbing ever faster;
she scratches, pummels you with small fists,
fastens her teeth in your neck,
doing unto you what you've often done unto her.

The *Kama Sutra* says that when the woman takes on the man's role, she has the choice of three basic but famous lovemaking techniques:

The Samdamsha *or the Tongs*

When the woman uses the Mare's Trick, gripping the penis tightly with her vagina, squeezing and stroking it alternatively and holding it inside her for a hundred heartbeats, it is known as *Samdamsha*.

A desire that arises spontaneously increases with experience. From mutual understanding comes ardour, which gradually becomes a permanent feeling.

The Bhramara *or the Buzzing Bee*

If, drawing up her feet, she revolves her hips in a circular motion so that the penis circles deep within the vagina much like a bee buzzing around a honey filled flower, it is called the *Bhramara*.

The Prenkholita *or the Swing*

If she swings her hips in wide circles and makes figures-of-eight, swaying upon on the man's body as though she were riding on a seesaw, it is known as the *Prenkholita*.

Besides these three very widely used techniques, the *Kama Sutra* also offers several variations to the reverse or *Viparita Maithuna*:

Catching your penis, the lady
with dark eyes like upturned lotus petals
guides it into her yoni,
clings to you and shakes her buttocks:
this is known as the *Charunarikshita* or Lovely Lady in Control.

Enthroned on your penis,
she places both hands on the bed

and makes love, while you
press your two hands to her thudding heart:
this is the *Lilasana* or Seat of Sport.

She sits upright upon you,
her head thrown back like a rearing mare,
bringing her feet together
on the bed to one side of your body:
this is called the *Hansabandha* or the Swan.

The young woman has one foot
on your heart and the other on the bed.
Bold, saucy women adore this posture,
which is known to the world
as the *Upavitika* or the Sacred Thread.

If your lover, seated above you
with feet lotus-crossed
and her body held erect and still
makes love to you,
it is known as the *Yugmapada* or the Foot Yoke.

If she strides you,
facing your feet,

brings both her feet up to your thighs,
and works her hips frantically,
it is known as the *Hansa-lila* or Swan Sport.

If you lie flat on your back
with legs stretched out
and your lover sits astride you, facing away
and grasping your feet,
it is called the *Vrisha* or the Bull.

Lying upon you, your beloved
moves round like a wheel,
pressing hands one after the other on the bed,
kissing your body as she circles:
experts call this *Chakrabandha* or the Wheel.

Generalized postures apart, the *Kama Sutra* offers tailor-made solutions to meet the individual needs of the partners:

For New Couples

In the case of newly married couples or people attempting intercourse for the first time, the *Kama Sutra* recommends the simplest and most common of positions: the Missionary Position in which the man assumes the dominant role and control over the degree of stimulation that they get. The partner assumes a passive role in such a position. Some of the techniques used to create an intimate environment are eye-to-eye contact, guiding the partner's hip movements, massaging the neck and back, nibbling on the ears, necks or lips. One of the most tried and tested methods for intercourse, this face-to-face position is classic and universal that makes it possible to have many variations to make it more attractive and exciting. The mobility of the hands, the proximity of the faces and the comfort of the bodies are the advantages that made it famous.

This position is also one that many identify with love and romance, the beginnings of a relationship especially in very young couples. The

Facing page: *Mount the thighs of your spouse, assist yourself with your hands, cleave to her and full of joy unite together so that the sun god will grant you a long life.*

first impression could well become the lasting impression and when good beginnings are made, with patience and care this position sets off first time partners well on the path to explore their sexuality with imagination and vigour.

For More Creative Couples

A slightly more advanced position than the basic Missionary Position, this has both people involved in switching their leg positions. The woman closes her legs, while the man straddles her. The benefit here is simple: for the man on top, additional stimulation to the penis and for the woman beneath, additional sensations in her inner thighs.

For Those Who Are Big Built

This is a variation on the Missionary Position. The passive person, the woman usually, sits on the edge of a chair or bed, and the man kneels in front of her and uses his hips to thrust forward. Thus neither person is placing any weight on the other. This however requires more co-ordination than the Missionary Position and is also considered less intimate. However, it allows for more foreplay as the man is in an excellent position to explore his partner's genitals with his eyes, hands or mouth.

For The Advanced and Adventurous

This is a reversal of the normal Missionary Position, where the couple is positioned head-to-head and toe-to-toe. Then one person reverses his stance, so that the man and the woman are now facing each head-to-toe and toe-to-head. The angle of entry is very different than what most couples are used to and is a great position for people with a sense of humour and adventure. Both partners should absolutely ensure that their feet are clean and sweet smelling!

Facing page: Sitting is a wonderful position to be intimate. It helps keep eye contact while kissing and caressing each other.

For Lazy Couples Who Prefer to Sit

This one is meant for those who want leisurely intimacy. Here the man and woman sit face-to-face. The man sits cross-legged on the bed or floor and the woman sits on top straddling him. This is a wonderful position to be intimate, make eye contact, kiss and whisper into each other's ears. Since stability is a key factor here, many people prefer facing the opposite direction, which makes for a more secure position. Since the angle for intercourse is not conducive to vigorous thrusting, this is a perfect posture for those who feel embarrassed when facing their partners.

For Pregnant Women

A man experiences pleasure up to ejaculation, while the woman's pleasure is continuous. When he has ejected his semen, he seeks rest, she is disappointed and wishes to continue.

This position, wherein both partners lie side-by-side, is recommended when the woman is pregnant. In this position, which can be very intimate, the couple spoons together. This is a perfect way to hug the

person and feel wanted and protected. The man is generally at the back and to make her vagina easily accessible for penetration the woman tilts her pelvis.

Ten Types of Blows

Positions apart, the *Kama Sutra* also recommends the innovative use of the penis during the act of making love. The *Kama Sutra* says that during intercourse ten types of blows may be struck with the penis, but of these only the most natural or *Upasripta* that is instinctive to even the most untutored man will result in clitoral stimulation. This is a gentle forward stroke that may be varied for depth and speed, allowing for a subtle, rhythm and spontaneity, which the other nine types of blows lack.

The other nine are:
* Grasping the penis and moving it in circles inside the *yoni*, is called *Manthana* or Churning.

Variety in postures literally opens up innumerable possibilities and variations that help keep the sexual frisson alive.

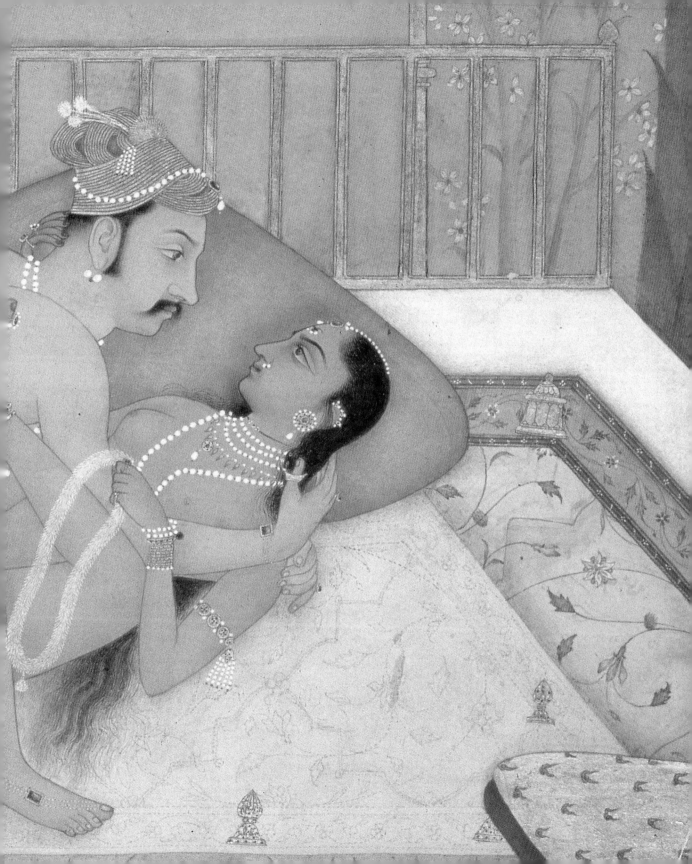

* When the penis is thrust sharply into the *yoni*, it is the *Hula* or Double-edged Knife. When the lady's hips are raised by a pillow, and the man strikes a rising blow, it is known as the *Avamardana* or Rubbing.

* If with breathlessness, the penis is pressed deep inside the womb it is called the *Piditaka* or Pressing.

* Hitting of groin with the genital organ. This *asana*, called *Piritak*, leads to tremendous excitement in both the partners.

* Withdrawing completely, if the womb is struck violently by the penis, the *asana* is known as the *Nirghata* or Buffet.

* If the penis is continuously pressed on one side of the vagina the *asana* is known as the *Varahaghata* or Boar's Blow.

* If the man thrusts wildly in every direction, like a bull tossing its horns, it is known as the *Vrishaghata* or the Bull's Blow.

Making love to two women who like each other and have the same tastes is called group sex. When performed with several women, it is known as the 'herd of cows'.

Different Types of Congress

Physical competence is one aspect of lovemaking, the other more important component are emotions. The *Kama Sutra* further classifies various kinds of intercourse depending on the kind of emotions and people involved. Vatsyayana describes various kinds of congress:

Loving Congress

When a man and a woman, who have been in love with each other for some time, come together with great difficulty, or when one of the two returns from a journey, or is reconciled after having been separated on account of a quarrel, their sexual union is called the loving congress. It is carried on according to the liking of the lovers, and for as long as they choose.

Congress of Subsequent Love

When two persons come together, while their love for each other is still in its infancy, their lovemaking is called the congress of subsequent love.

When he comes to see her, he brings the girl he is courting, garlands of flowers, refined beauty products and other gifts.

Congress of Spontaneous Love

The congress that takes place between two persons who are attached to one another, and which is done according to their own liking is called the congress of spontaneous love.

Congress of Artificial Love

When a man initiates intercourse by exciting himself by means of the sixty-four ways, such as kissing, or when a man and a woman come together, though in reality they are both attached to different persons, this kind of sex is then called the congress of artificial love.

Congress of Transferred Love

When a man, from the beginning to the end of the congress, thinks all the time that he is enjoying another one whom he loves, it is called the congress of transferred love.

Congress of Eunuchs

The congress between a man and a female water carrier, or a female servant or a person of a lower caste, lasting only until desire is satisfied, is called congress like that of eunuchs. Here foreplay and external touching, kissing, and manipulation are not to be employed.

Deceitful Congress

The congress between a courtesan and a rustic, or between citizens and other women of the village or bordering countries, is called deceitful congress.

Intercourse with Courtesans and Other Women

Notwithstanding the classifications and despite being well-versed in all the arts and techniques of lovemaking, the sage Vatsyanana acknowledged that wives eventually will tire their husbands and as a result justifies men seeking other outlets for seeking sexual stimuli. In this connection, the *Kama Sutra* explores the possibilities of seeking gratification by seducing the wives of other men, who are seen as exciting, challenging, worthy of indefatigable pursuit besides being great

Facing page: Once pleasure has been awakened having scented her with flower essences and offered her betel, he stimulates her by his embraces and begins erotic games.

fun in bed. It is also uninhibited in its acknowledgement of men seeking out courtesans or *ganikas* as well as indulging in group sex, where many men may make love to one woman, or one man in turn makes love to many women. Vatsyayana believed that if passions cannot be gratified by normal sexual intercourse with just one man or woman, then it was permissible to have intercourse with a variety of men and women.

❋ Thus when one man enjoys two women at the same time, both of whom love him equally, it is called the united congress.

❋ When a man enjoys many women altogether, it is called the congress of a herd of cows.

❋ When many young men enjoy a woman who may be married to one of them, either one after the other, or at the same time. Then, one of them holds her, another enjoys her, a third uses her mouth, a fourth holds her middle part, and in this way they go on enjoying her several parts alternately.

❋ The same can be done when several men are sitting in company with one courtesan, or when one courtesan is alone with many men. In the same way this can be done by the women of the king's harem when they get hold of a man.

Imitation of Animals

At a time when society was agrarian and closely associated with nature, it is natural that some of the positions that are recommended in the *Kama Sutra* draw inspiration from nature, or from the animals that were domesticated and commonly observed. 'An ingenious person should multiply the kinds of congress after the fashion of the different kinds of beasts and of birds. For these different kinds of congress, performed according to the usage of each country, and the liking of each individual, generate love, friendship, and respect in the hearts of women.'

Every animal has its own peculiar mating pattern; and the men and women who observed this adopted it for themselves. The ways of cows,

Facing page: *Sexual relations can be diversified by studying the movements of domestic and wild animals as well as insects. Those who follow their fantasy inspire affection, desire and esteem in women.*

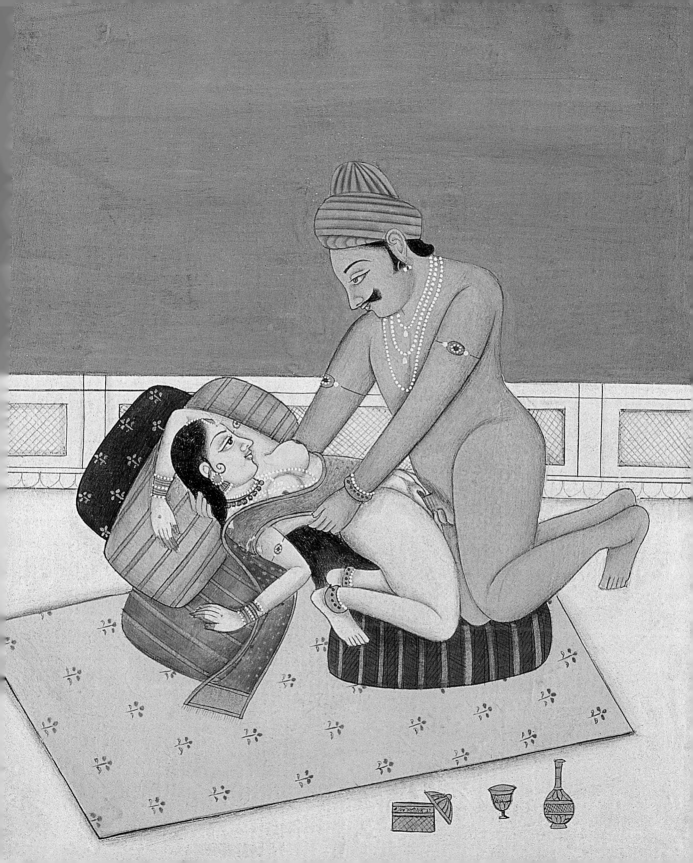

buffaloes, dogs, horses, goats, sheep as well as other animals in the wild, were observed and imitated adding variety and novelty to the sexual act. For example, when a woman is on her hands and feet like a quadruped, and her lover mounts her like a bull, it is called the congress of a cow. Similarly, there are positions called the congress of sporting in water, the congress of an elephant with many female elephants, the congress of goats, the congress of deer, the congress of a dog, the forcible mounting of an ass, the congress of a cat, the jump of a tiger, the pressing of an elephant, the rubbing of a boar, and the mounting of a horse.

Orgasm

The main endeavour of all intercourse is to experience orgasm that, according to the text, is the basic right of men and women. Keeping in mind the fact that women take longer to achieve orgasm the text, instructs men to treat women in such a way 'that she achieves her sexual climax first'.

For the uninitiated it explains in detail the physical attributes associated with climax: 'Shivering of hands is the first symptom that shows that the woman has reached the height of excitement.' At this stage, she shows deep love and does not allow her partner to withdraw even when the male has ejaculated. The quivering in her *yoni* is known as the *Chatakavilasa* or the Sparrow's Sport, and usually heralds orgasm. The involuntary shuddering of orgasm is called *Samputa*, the Jewel Case.

Vatsyayana also lays down rules for behaviour once intercourse is over. He recommends that the partners should not withdraw from each other immediately and must feel their presence inside each other for some time. This practice, he says helps to retain intimacy. Even after separation, he says the man should with his own hands apply pure sandalwood paste on the body of the woman and that subsequently the couple should sit together on the terrace in the moonlight, talk lovingly and eat and drink.

About these things there cannot be either enumeration or any definite rule. Intercourse, once commenced, passion alone gives birth to all the acts for both partners.

Facing page: *Whether they continue having sexual relations or live chastely with each other, true love between a couple never decreases even after a hundred years.*

Transcending Joy

Of all the energies present the most potent is sexual energy that is seen as one of God's gifts for it impels human beings to catch a glimpse of the divine...

The universal belief is that in the beginning there was chaos and from this disorder emerged the process of creation. From this order materialized the miracle of consciousness and simultaneously sexual differentiation. Thus the universe was viewed as not just sacred but essentially sexual as well.

In their attempt to visualize the origins of life, the ancients personified *Kama* as the first principle of desire and made attempts, often erotically, to explain the unknown as symbols and myths narrated in tales, poetry, ballads and drama. At the core of these myths lies the idea that the duality that resulted at creation forever sought to re-unite with the first principle. The highest aim in human life thus was to seek the intrinsic and underlying oneness with nature. Given the pluralism of Indian thought, the human body became one amongst several accepted paths to seek the divine within oneself.

One school of thought believed that through sexual union one could connect to the very source of creation and this connection was what lifted human consciousness from the ordinary into a higher plane. Hence sexuality was considered to be an affirmation of life, a way of living, the purpose of life being to seek pleasure and find the means to experience ecstasy.

Today sexuality is a much-maligned aspect regarded sometimes as the baser and lower instinct of human life. But this was not always so and certainly not in India. Ancient sages had an open attitude towards sexuality and instead of being burdened by inhibitions, people were encouraged to learn about their sexuality and develop the art of loving through education and practice. Satisfaction in every sphere of life was considered the characteristic of a civilized society and to this end every aspect of life was researched and explained in elaborate treatises.

Viewed thus, sexuality and, as a result, the body became a doorway to spiritual evolution. So the coming together of a man and woman was seen as sacred and this idea became the touchstone of Indian philosophy. Sexuality in all its forms was worthy of reverence from the very inception of time, for it was from the coming together of a man and a woman, and the energy that emanated from this union, that created life. So, to separate the two, categorizing the body as gross and the spirit as divine was not just erroneous but anathema, and went against the grain of fundamental Hindu belief.

There was a sacred component in every activity. Whether it was eating, drinking, tasting, touching or making love, each action was a form of *rasa*, a creative expression of desire. The Hindus believed that these tremendous forces of desire could be transmuted into the highest form of spiritual energy, not by renunciation, but by submission to it. Of these energies the most potent was sexual energy that was seen as one of God's gifts, for it impelled humans to catch a glimpse of the divine. Cosmic energy was present in all living beings as the sex force was

The tide of desire runs through both good and evil. Man must endeavour to make the tide of desire turn to the right way.

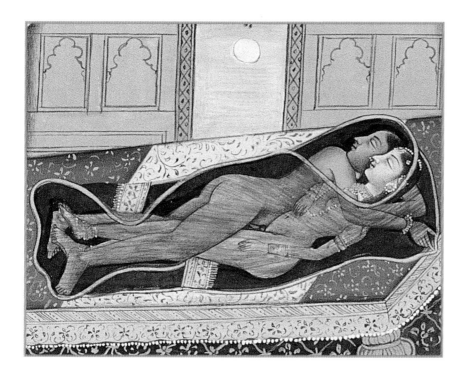

sacred, worthy of being worshipped and not frittered away. So sex, rather than being opposed to the spirit was in fact its ally. This energy could be tapped if sexuality was worshipped as the primal force or Shakti, the feminine counterpart to Shiva, the male dimension. So the coming together of man and woman, who symbolically represented Shiva and Shakti, was to establish the balance needed for human life that made the world whole, dynamic, loving, and fruitful. Sexual love and religion thus became the two most favoured paths to the fulfillment of a universal wish of seeking merger with the higher consciousness.

Sexuality in itself is much more than an act of intercourse. The moment when two sets of eyes meet, when hands touch for the very first time, the sensation when lips kiss, the warm breath against naked skin—every touch, sight, smell and sound is an emotionally charged erotic moment to be savoured and cherished. Seen as the very essence of desire, the physicality of sex cannot be separated from the erotic for without eroticism the physicality of sex is considered empty.

When all desires have been satisfied, the root of discernment is firmly planted. On the way to spiritual realization, the realization of desires is essential.

The Kama Sutra

These concepts had been in practice for over 2000 years, long before the *Kama Sutra* was written. So to the sage Vatsyayana the idea that the body was as sacred as the spirit was hardly revolutionary. The essential principle that the *Kama Sutra* keeps emphasizing on is the importance of balance, of seeking all aspects of life in the right proportions. This openness about sexuality was tempered with morality and ethical social behaviour. The right manner to live life was to strike the right balance between all human urges: physical, emotional, intellectual, social, sexual as well as spiritual.

According to the Vedic tradition, human beings are governed by a four-fold structure: *Artha* or external security and contentment; *Kama* or fulfillment of desires; *Dharma* or leading life according to natural laws; *Moksha* or evolution towards ultimate freedom.

It was believed that human life was precious because only human beings had self-awareness and the potential to realize the higher consciousness. So this quest to seek union with the higher consciousness was seen as the fundamental purpose of human life. The scriptures therefore recommended that a man should attempt to live on various planes and that he should neither ignore his spiritual needs nor his social obligations and duties to family, community and career. Nor should he ignore his sensuality, his need for love and erotic fulfillment. Vatsyayana's vision of balance was based on this wholeness, an all encompassing ideal where every situation provided an opportunity to become more self-aware and helped in expanding one's capacities. Nor was this learning confined to the physical act, rather it included even the environment, location, behaviour, cleanliness of the body, decorousness of manners, allurement, a knowledge of all the arts, a fine sense of aesthetics—all of which came together to work miracles.

The *Kama Sutra* enumerates some concepts that went on to become the basic tenets of Tantra, although in itself it is not a tantric text. Its advice: Lovemaking is not only pleasurable and necessary for procreation, it is also a vehicle for spiritual awakening, helping couples find harmony and bliss, rather than strife and selfishness, within the sexual act. The first step towards this direction was to have the right knowledge, and

Facing page: The quest to seek union with the higher consciousness is seen as the fundamental purpose of human life.

understanding the *Kama Shastras* would help men evolve from animality to humanity and thence to seek the divine. That would push them forward from being less conscious to more conscious beings. Such awareness brought with it the imperative to seek the higher consciousness and thus encouraged men to engage in correct sexual intercourse as a spiritual discipline rather than for purely hedonistic reasons.

Tantra

The same principles emerged a few centuries later as Tantric practices. An important sub sect of Hinduism, it recognized the importance of sexual freedom in the liberation of the soul and accepted sex as an important means to experience bliss as well as to physically experience God. Tantra taught its followers to revere their sexual partners and to transform the act of sex into a sacrament. The word '*tantra*' in Sanskrit means, 'weaving' and is often interpreted as the weaving of the masculine and feminine principles. The act of creation as visualized by the ancients, based on their observance of nature, got manifested in the coming together of man and woman as the duality of the sexes. The principle of Tantra sought to merge the disparate natures of man and woman into an ecstatic union. The concepts of masculine and feminine were thus viewed as two polarities that through the very powerful energy of love could come together and help human beings experience an altered mystical state of consciousness. Wholeness thus became holiness, representing union with the divine.

Tantrics believe that the few moments prior to orgasm are much like meditation and produce the same euphoric effects. Orgasm is akin to a preview of *samadhi* or oneness with a higher consciousness, albeit on a smaller and temporary scale, but is able to produce the same states of rapture. Just prior to ejaculation the mind is in its purest form, single pointed and focused, and at this point one transcends one's bodies. When the mind becomes devoid of thought, when the sense of 'I' disappears even momentarily, when the egocentric view of the world is set aside, when one is focused entirely on the bliss of the moment, one enters an altered state of being very much like achieving 'god consciousness'.

Facing page: Tantrics believe that orgasm produces the same euphoric feelings as meditation and is akin, at least temporarily, to liberation.

Modern psychologists too concede that this potent sexual energy can be sublimated into higher avenues—typically into art and spirituality. 'Elements of the sexual instinct are characterized by a capacity for sublimation, for changing sexual desire into a different, more socially worthy one. To the sum of these energies, we probably owe the highest results of our culture,' wrote Sigmund Freud. He added that the basis for our need to love lies in the experience of separateness and the resulting need to keep the experience of union.

Apart from pointing the way to divinity, sexuality is thus also creative and forms the basis of aesthetics and all art forms. *'Maithunam paramam tatvam, shrushti stithi anya karanam…*(Coition is the ultimate principle behind creation, preservation and destruction of the Universe),' says Lord Shiva in the *Kailash Tantra*. Sexuality thus found expression in art, literature, sculpture, poetry, dramaturgy, theology, in fact in every aspect of human life. Like its literature, Indian art too became quite explicit in exploring the erotic; no expression of life was left unexplored: there are depictions of men and women engaged with one another, with multiple partners, animals and inanimate objects. Celibacy, monogamy, polygamy and polyandry—all had a place. In their firm belief that sexuality was a metaphor for the union of the human soul with the divine, much of Indian art blends divinity with sensuality. Depictions ranging from the sexual and autoerotic attitudes of men and women, including gods and goddesses, members of the aristocracy. Ascetics to group sexuality and bestiality were displayed ostentatiously on the exteriors and in the interiors of the temples. Their walls may well have been the visual interpretations of passages from the *Kama Sutra* and other erotic texts.

All Hindu art, especially sculpture and metal iconography, depicted goddesses as voluptuously curved women. Parvati the most beautiful of them all is slender waisted, with heavy breasts and hips, as were Lakshmi, Saraswati and all other major and minor goddesses. The same was true of paintings. Although most of these paintings did not have a religious function, they were often based on religious or mythological subjects that were treated sensuously. Themes such as the *nayika bheda* (differentiation of heroes and heroines) or the *ragamala* (garland of musical modes, dealing with melodic themes) all combined desire and devotion in ingenious ways. In art and literature Lord Krishna came to epitomize the archetypal hero and Radha the ideal heroine. Their physical yearning for each other was regarded as a metaphor for the soul's craving for union with the divine. Thus viewed there was no place for ordinary sex. Every intercourse became mystical and even mundane sex was elevated to a spiritual plane.

Conflict Between Ascetic and Erotic

While few doubt the connection between sexual and spiritual energies, a polarity emerged between the two. Paradoxically Indian tradition supports both the ideals—eroticism as well as asceticism. While one school of thought used sexuality to enhance spirituality, the other believed that to increase spirituality, one should sublimate one's sexual energies. The conflict between the ascetic and the erotic, between passion and *vairagya* or world-weariness, between birth and death, is best expressed by the myth of the burning of Kamadeva, the God of Desire, by Lord Shiva. Shiva's resolve to remain an ascetic was considered inimical to the continuity of life and, hence, Kamadeva was assigned the task of distracting him to keep the process of creation alive. The Lord disturbed during his penance opened his third eye and burned Kamadeva to cinders. But he was promptly brought back to life at the behest of Rati and Parvati as well as all the gods because without Kamadeva, there would be no procreation. This dichotomy between asceticism and eroticism was thus resolved not by denying the existence of desire and sexual pleasure but by sublimating

The dichotomy between asceticism and eroticism was resolved not by denying desire but by sublimating these desires to a higher state of being.

these desires for a higher state of being. Either way, the quest was to seek bliss or *Ananda*.

The sexual act however brought but limited and transient satisfaction. How could one extend this experience? The *Shastras* recommend two paths—the first to extend the brief experience into a longer one by developing single-pointedness that directs the orgasmic energy inwards; the second path is to transcend the sexual experience and channel the sexual energy elsewhere to creative works, to heal oneself, to meditate and to attempt to experience this energy in all nature without involving the sexual act. This brings us to celibacy.

Celibacy

Nature follows a fixed path and therefore even transcending sexuality will follow its own natural course, for, by the time man reaches middle age, the preoccupation with sex will leave him. He may still have sex but will be detached, therefore naturally veering towards becoming celibate. So the ancients did not see celibacy as the killing of sexual energy but the channelling of sexual energies to other areas of life. It is the transcending of sexual, bodily pleasure derived from our senses to the experience of reality beyond the senses. Celibacy was seen as the ability

to find and experience ecstasy within oneself and redirect sexual energies towards more meditative or spiritual experiences. It was the withdrawal of the mind and body from the senses.

Its been acknowledged that the sexual struggle and power equations between men and women is often a reflection of the broader struggle between man and god. Sexual disconnectedness is often viewed as a reflection of a larger disconnectedness with the world. Strengthening inter-personal relationships is one way of ensuring that one's connectedness with the divine is also strengthened. The extent to which we love ourselves and those around us would reflect the degree to which we would be closer to the divine. Transcending sexuality would help us maximize pleasure and minimize pain, and through extremely sensuous lovemaking visualize the sacred. Therefore the first step towards pleasure and happiness is to experience oneness with other beings, nature and the world, and not see oneself as a fragmented being.

The *Kama Sutra* taught a yogic art that helped explore the hidden dimensions of the unity of the body and the mind, which modern science is only now beginning to acknowledge. Viewed from today's perspective the *Kama Sutra* presents to us a radically different view about sexuality: sex is a lawful, if limited, expression of bliss and as a means of getting in touch with a higher consciousness.

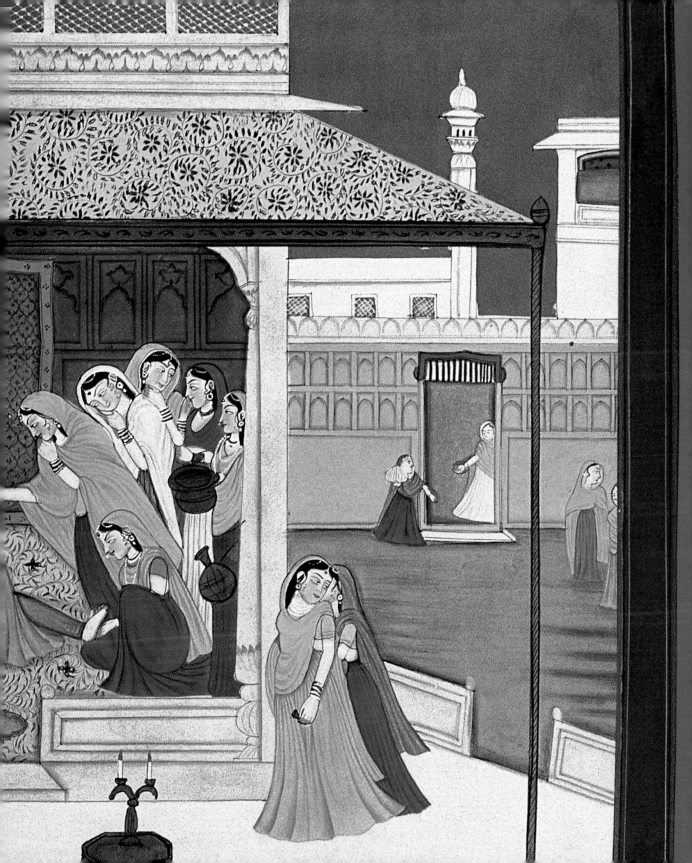

ISBN: 81-7436-319-X

Text:
© Sandhya Mulchandani 2004

Photographs and Documents:
© Roli Collection and Sandhya Mulchandani

Roli Books Team:
Dipa Chaudhuri, Arati Subramanyam,
Naresh Mondal, Narendar Kr. Shahi, Naresh Nigam

Roli & Janssen BV 2004
Published in India by
Roli Books in arrangement
with Roli & Janssen BV
M-75 Greater Kailash-II (Market)
New Delhi 110 048, India.
Phone: ++91-11-29212271, ++91-11-29212782
Fax: ++91-11-29217185
Email: roli@vsnl.com
Website: rolibooks.com

Printed and bound in Singapore